Seven
Solid
States

THE GENERAL CHEMISTRY MONOGRAPH SERIES

Russell Johnsen, Editor

Florida State University

Gordon M. Barrow (*Case Institute of Technology*)	THE STRUCTURE OF MOLECULES
Fred Basolo (*Northwestern University*), Ronald C. Johnson (*Emory University*)	COORDINATION CHEMISTRY
Gregory R. Choppin (*Florida State University*)	NUCLEI AND RADIO-ACTIVITY
Werner Herz (*Florida State University*)	THE SHAPE OF CARBON COMPOUNDS
Robin M. Hochstrasser (*University of Pennsylvania*)	BEHAVIOR OF ELECTRONS IN ATOMS
Ronald C. Johnson (*Emory University*)	INTRODUCTORY DESCRIPTIVE CHEMISTRY
Edward L. King (*University of Colorado*)	HOW CHEMICAL REACTIONS OCCUR
Edwin M. Larsen (*University of Wisconsin*)	TRANSITIONAL ELEMENTS
Bruce H. Mahan (*University of California*)	ELEMENTARY CHEMICAL THERMODYNAMICS
Walter J. Moore (*Indiana University*)	SEVEN SOLID STATES

Seven
Solid States

An Introduction
to the Chemistry and Physics of Solids

Walter J. Moore

Indiana University

1967

W. A. BENJAMIN, INC.   New York   Amsterdam

SEVEN SOLID STATES
An Introduction to the Chemistry and Physics of Solids

Library of Congress Catalog Card Number 67-19435
Manufactured in the United States of America

*The manuscript was put into production on November 11, 1966;
this volume was published on June 19, 1967*

W. A. BENJAMIN, INC.
New York, New York 10016

Editor's Foreword

THE TEACHING OF INTRODUCTORY CHEMISTRY becomes each day a more challenging and rewarding task as subject matter becomes more diverse and more complex and as the high school preparation of the student improves. These challenges have evoked a number of responses; this series of monographs for general chemistry is one such. It is an experiment in the teaching of chemistry which recognizes a number of the problems that confront those who select textbooks and teach chemistry. First of all, it is recognized that no single book can physically encompass all of the various aspects of chemistry that all instructors collectively deem important. Second, it is admitted that no single author is capable of writing authoritatively on *all* of the topics that are included in everybody's list of what constitutes introductory chemistry. Finally, it recognizes the instructor's right to choose those topics which he considers to be important without having to apologize for having omitted large parts of an extensive textbook.

This volume, then, is one of approximately fifteen in the General Chemistry Monograph Series, each written by one or more highly qualified persons very familiar with the current status of the subject by virtue of research in it, but also conversant with the problems associated with teaching the subject matter to beginning students. Each volume deals broadly with one of the subdivisions of general chemistry or areas directly impinging on it and constitutes a complete entity, far more comprehensive in coverage than is permitted by the limitations of the standard one-volume text. Taken together these volumes provide a range of topics from which the individual instructor can easily select those which will provide for his class an appropriate coverage of the material he considers most important.

Furthermore, coverage of a number of topics only recently being considered for introductory chemistry courses, such as thermodynamics, molecular spectroscopy, reaction kinetics and mechanism, atomic spectroscopy, photochemistry, and biochemistry is or will soon be available. In every instance a modern structural point of view has been adopted. The emphasis is on general principles and unifying theory, but with adequate reference to experiments.

These materials will have other uses also; selected volumes can be used to enrich the more conventional course of study by providing readily available inexpensive supplements to standard texts. They should also prove valuable to students in other areas of the physical and biological sciences needing supplementary information in the field of chemistry pertinent to their own special interests. Thus, students of biology should find the monographs on biochemistry, organic chemistry, coordination chemistry, and reaction kinetics particularly useful. Beginning students in physics and meteorology will find the monographs on thermodynamics and atomic structure rewarding. Teachers of elementary science will also find these invaluable aids to bringing them up to date in the various branches of chemistry. The monograph on nuclei and radioactivity should prove useful to anyone interested in the application of radioisotopes to experimental problems.

It is hoped that titles will continue to be added as new areas come into the purview of introductory chemistry. Suggestions for additions to the series will be welcomed by the editor.

RUSSELL JOHNSEN

Tallahassee, Florida
April 1965

Preface

Now after all this to lerne ye had need,
Of seven circulations of Elements for your speede.
According to number of the Planets seaven;
Which no man knoweth but he have grace from heaven.
Old Philosophers men of great engine,
Said how of circulations there shulde be Nine;
It is the surer to doe by their advice,
Nethles seaven may your works suffice.

Thomas Norton of Bristoll, c. 1420.

The solid state is a subject that ought to be of major interest to students of chemistry. In a world filled with lasers, masers, phosphors, ferrites, thermistors, transistors—and Xerox—there is no need to stress the practical importance of solid state devices. It has been estimated that about one third of all physicists engaged in research are at work on some aspect of the science of solids. Many of the most imaginative scientists of our times have made their marks in this field: Einstein, Debye, Wigner, Mott, Wagner, Pauling, Frenkel, and Schottky, are a few who immediately come to mind. Chemistry itself is sometimes considered to be essentially "the science of materials," and most of these materials are solids. The theory of solids provides some of our best insights into the nature of the forces that bind together atoms, ions, and molecules. Because structures in a solid are fixed in space, it is possible to perform on them a variety of experiments that depend on the directions of imposed electric and magnetic fields, while such directional experiments would not be possible with gaseous or liquid substances. In short, there are rather impressive reasons why a prospective chemist should become acquainted with the solid state, and should do so nearly at the outset of his studies.

Nevertheless, it is quite possible at present for a chemistry student to reach his senior year at a university with only a most superficial knowledge of how solids are constructed and how they behave. The subject of the solid state seems to be particularly neglected in first-year chemistry courses, while properties of gases, liquid solutions, and isolated small molecules are often discussed in some detail. Therefore, this book was written as an attempt to inspire in beginning students an interest in the science of solid materials.

In order to bring out the practical relevance of the theoretical discussions, I have chosen seven exemplary solids, which are familiar to every beginning chemist. Then I have tried to show in some depth what we know about each of these substances. It is evident, of course, that the chosen examples illustrate general principles that can be applied to other solids also. Thus the story of sodium chloride introduces the theory of ionic crystals. What is said about gold is usually valid for silver and often for other metals. The discussion of nickel oxide introduces the vast domain of nonstoichiometric inorganic compounds, and so on.

It is hoped that this book will kindle enough interest to lead you much further into the subject. It is not meant to be a Baedeker precisely listing every curiosity in a foreign land. It is more like one of those colorful booklets published by the airlines, tempting a prospective traveler to rush out and buy his ticket to Kyoto or Belo Horizonte. To buy now and pay later perhaps, for it must be admitted that some sections of this book will demand careful study from even a good student.

This nonuniform level of difficulty is more or less deliberate. It stems from the idea that learning, in the first place, is simply a process of becoming familiar with something strange. We can become familiar with a subject before we really understand it (as etymology indicates and any family member can testify). In a developing science, our understanding must, in fact, be always in a process of evolution. Thus I hoped that a student might first read this book during the second half of his freshman year—after he had learned some elementary thermodynamics and atomic structure. Then, he might use it again later, as a supplement to his study of physical chemistry and physics.

In writing this book, I made frequent use of several basic works on the solid state. I wish to express my debt to the authors of these and hope that the student also will turn to them for deeper understanding. Particular mention should be made of *Introduction to Solid State Physics* by C. Kittel and *Principles of the Theory of Solids* by J. M. Ziman. At a less advanced level, *Introduction to Solids* by L. Azaroff and *Physics of Solids* by C. A. Wert and R. M. Thomson can be highly recommended.

WALTER J. MOORE

Bloomington, Indiana
April 1967

Contents

I

Salt

A FLAMMABLE SILVERY metal seizes electrons from a deadly green gas, and the resultant positive and negative ions line up into tasty crystals of common salt, NaCl. Its chemical name is *sodium chloride* and its geological name is *rock salt*. Crystalline NaCl is the prototype of ionic crystals, which include a large proportion of all natural and synthetic inorganic substances. The first exact work on crystal structures was done on crystals of NaCl and KCl, and the alkali halides have been studied in more quantitative detail than any other crystals. Thus NaCl is an almost inevitable choice to introduce the solid state.

1.1 CRYSTAL SYMMETRY

From solution in pure water, NaCl crystallizes in the form of cubes. This is the cubic *habit* of the substance. The cube is a highly symmetrical solid figure, that is to say, we can think of many operations that bring it into coincidence with itself. Any such operation is called a *symmetry operation*. An example is rotation of a cube by 90° about an axis passing through midpoints of a pair of opposite faces. One of these three axes, labeled C_4, is shown in Fig. 1.1. They are called 4-fold symmetry axes. A cube also has other symmetry axes: six 2-fold axes (C_2—180° rotors) passing through the midpoints of opposite edges, and four 3-fold axes (C_3—120° rotors) passing through opposite corners. Besides its symmetry axes, a cube has other symmetry elements. If we slice a cube in half normal to a C_4 axis and insert a mirror in the cut, the reflection of one half-cube in the mirror exactly coincides with the

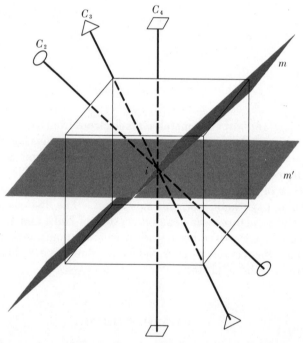

Fig. 1.1. Symmetry elements of the cube as displayed by crystals of rock salt.

other half-cube. Thus we say that the plane of the slice is a *mirror plane* or *plane of symmetry*, denoted by *m*. It is evident that there are three such mirror planes, one perpendicular to each of the C_4 axes. In addition the cube has six diagonal planes of symmetry (one is shown in Fig. 1.1), one normal to each of the C_2 axes.

In addition to its C's and m's the cube has a further element of symmetry, namely, a *center of symmetry* or *inversion center, i*. If all the points that outline the cube are projected through *i*, the cube again comes into coincidence with itself.

Thus we describe the high symmetry of a cube in terms of its symmetry elements: three C_4, four C_3, six C_2, three *m* perpendicular to C_4, six *m* perpendicular to C_2, and *i*. It should be noted that more than one symmetry operation can belong to a given symmetry *element*. Thus C_4 can perform the symmetry operations of rotation by 90°, 180°, 270°, and 360°. These operations would be written, $C_4(\pi/2)$, $C_4(\pi)$, $C_4(3\pi/2)$, $C_4(2\pi)$.

1.2 POINT GROUPS

The set of all symmetry operations of a finite figure, such as a cube, forms a *group*. The concept of group, as defined in mathematics, is a set of members that obey the following rules:

Group Postulates

(1) If A and B are members of the group the product[1] $AB = C$ is also a member of the group.

(2) The set contains a unit member E such that RE equals R for all members R in the group.

(3) The set contains for every member R an *inverse*, which may be called R^{-1}, such that $RR^{-1} = E$ for all R in the group.

We can prove for ourselves that the set of symmetry operations of a cube obeys all the group postulates.[2] These operations,

---

[1] In this connotation the "product AB" means the operation B followed by the operation A.

[2] Just as an example of postulate (1): If m_1 is the mirror plane normal to the 4-fold axis $C_4^{(1)}$, $m_1 C_4^{(1)}(\pi) = i$. Rotation of π radians (180°) followed by reflection in the plane m_1 is equivalent to inversion through the center of symmetry. An example of postulate (3): $C_4(\pi/2) C_4(3\pi/2) = E$.

therefore, constitute the *symmetry group* of a cube. This particular group is given the symbol O_h. It is called a *point group* since each operation leaves at least one point in the figure unchanged. A little thought will indicate that any symmetry operation applied to a finite figure must leave at least one point unchanged. In the case of i, this point is the center of symmetry itself. In the case of a C, all points on the axis are invariant; in the case of m, all points in the plane.

Although NaCl forms cubic crystals, it is not obvious without further examination that these crystals are strictly comparable in symmetry with the ideal geometric figure of a cube. Suppose, for instance, one face of the NaCl cubic crystal was always red. Such a solid would certainly be less symmetrical than the ideal cube. "But that is ridiculous," you may say, and to be sure we should be surprised to find a salt crystal with a red face. It is not unusual, however, to find substances in which corresponding faces in crystals differ in surface texture. The cubic crystals of iron pyrites, for instance, have different striations on different faces. As a consequence the C_4 axes are reduced to C_2 axes and the six C_2 axes with m's normal to them are lost. The point group of iron pyrites crystals is called T_h, and it has a lower symmetry than the full cubic symmetry represented by rock salt.

1.3   CRYSTAL SYSTEMS

Actual crystals of a given substance may vary in size and shape as a consequence of different conditions of growth, but it is usually possible to obtain some specimens with well-developed faces. We often need to refer to particular crystal faces and a convenient notation has been invented for this purpose.

The faces of crystals can be designated by means of a set of three noncoplanar axes. The particular set of axes we use depends on the symmetry of the crystal. If we draw the axes so that their lengths are in definite ratios for a given crystalline substance (but independent of the particular crystal we have in hand), a remarkable law of nature can be observed. Consider in Fig. 1.2 three axes

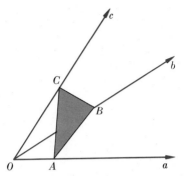

Fig. 1.2. A crystal plane intercepts a set of crystal axes.

with lengths a, b, c, which are cut by plane ABC, making intercepts OA, OB, OC. Expressed as fractions of the crystal axes, these lengths are OA/a, OB/b, and OC/c. The reciprocals of these lengths are a/OA, b/OB, and c/OC. The *law of rational intercepts* now states that these reciprocal intercepts will always be in the ratio of whole numbers (hkl) for planes which are crystal faces. It is called the "law of rational intercepts" because the intercepts themselves can always be expressed as ratios of rational numbers and hence can be reduced to whole numbers by appropriate multiplication factors. In 1839, W. H. Miller introduced these reciprocal intercepts to designate crystal faces. They can also be used to designate planes within crystals. If a face is parallel to a given axis the intercept is at infinity, and the corresponding Miller index must be $1/\infty = 0$.

Depending on the axes required for the law of rational intercepts to hold, all crystals can be divided into seven distinct classes. These are called the *seven crystal systems*. They are summarized in Table 1.1.

1.4 MILLER INDICES FOR ROCK SALT CRYSTALS

In Fig. 1.3 we show Miller indices for rock salt crystals. The six faces are designated as (100) ($\bar{1}$00) (010) (0$\bar{1}$0) (001) (00$\bar{1}$).

Table 1.1   Crystal Systems and Bravais Lattices

System	Axes	Angles	Bravais Lattices
1. Cubic	$a = b = c$	$\alpha = \beta = \gamma = 90°$	1. Simple
			2. Face-centered
			3. Body-centered
2. Tetragonal	$a = b;\ c$	$\alpha = \beta = \gamma = 90°$	4. Simple
			5. Body-centered
3. Orthorhombic	$a;\ b;\ c$	$\alpha = \beta = \gamma = 90°$	6. Simple
			7. End-centered
			8. Face-centered
			9. Body-centered
4. Rhombohedral	$a = b = c$	$\alpha = \beta = \gamma$	10. Simple
5. Hexagonal	$a = b;\ c$	$\alpha = \beta = 90°;$ $\gamma = 120°$	11. Simple
6. Monoclinic	$a;\ b;\ c$	$\alpha = \gamma = 90°;\ \beta$	12. Simple
			13. Side-centered
7. Triclinic	$a;\ b;\ c$	$\alpha;\ \beta;\ \gamma$	14. Simple

Note that in the Miller index for a crystal face only the ratio $h:k:l$ is significant. Thus (220) would be the same face as (110). On the other hand, for planes within crystals multiplication by an integer would change the interplanar spacing. Thus the planes 200 would include the 100 and in addition the set midway between them. Note the usage (hkl) to refer to crystal faces and hkl (without parentheses) to refer to sets of planes. If we wish to refer to all the equivalent planes or faces of a crystal, that is, a *form* of a crystal, we use curly brackets. For example, we would say that the cubic sodium chloride has the $\{100\}$ form.

The direction of a line in a crystal is given by a symbol $[uvw]$. We place the origin of coordinates at one point on the line and then write down the coordinates of a second point to define the line. For example, suppose we go a distance x/a along the x axis and distance y/b along the y axis and distance z/c along the z axis. When $x/a, y/b, z/c$ are reduced to the set of smallest integers in the same ratio, they are indices of the direction of the line and written

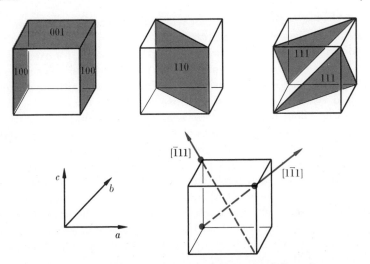

Fig. 1.3.   Miller indices of crystal planes and directions.

[uvw].   Note particularly that reciprocals are not used in the designation of the indices of a direction line.   We show the [111] and [1$\bar{1}$1] directions in Fig. 1.3.

If sodium chloride crystallizes from aqueous solution containing increasing concentrations of urea, the crystals are no longer perfect cubes, but octahedral faces begin to develop, until finally at concentrations greater than about 8.5% urea, only octahedral faces are present.   A regular octahedron possesses all the symmetry elements of a cube, and thus octahedral crystals of sodium chloride, as they must, also belong to the class O_h.   The octahedral form is {111}, which is made up of eight faces (111), ($\bar{1}$11), etc.

1.5   RESTRICTIONS ON CRYSTAL SYMMETRY

If you consider again the Table 1.1 of crystal systems, you may notice a curious and important fact.   The systems allow different symmetry elements in the crystals, but the only kinds of axes that occur are C_2, C_3, C_4, and C_6.   There are no 5-fold axes,

7-fold axes, or 8-fold axes. The reason for this restriction is fundamental. There is nothing in the world to prevent an isolated molecule from having a 5-fold symmetry axis (ferrocene, for example).
Why do C_5 axes occur in molecules but not in crystals? The reason
is simply that it is impossible to fill all of space with figures of
5-fold symmetry. We can see this even in two dimensions. We
can tile a floor with equilateral triangles, with rectangles, or with
regular hexagons. We could not possibly do the job with regular
pentagons without leaving gaps in the flooring.

The absence in actual crystals of any axial symmetry elements
except 2-, 3-, 4-, and 6-fold axes therefore suggests an important
conclusion: crystals must be constructed of regular subunits which
fill all space in definite geometric array. The regular crystal forms
observed in nature are outward manifestations of inner regularities
in structure. We might have guessed this fact on general principles
and indeed it was suggested long ago by Robert Hooke and René
Haüy. The restrictions on allowed crystal axes, however, provide
the strongest support for the idea.

1.6   LATTICES AND CRYSTAL STRUCTURES

To describe a regular array of units in space we make use of a
mathematical concept called a *lattice*. A lattice is a regular infinite array of points in space arranged as the intersection points of
three ranges of equidistant planes (1). We can join these points in
various ways so as to make *unit cells*, which fill all space.

There are severe restrictions, as we have seen, on the kinds of
cells that can fill all space. Sometimes for convenience in descrip-
tion we do not use a cell in which all the points are at the corners
but instead use a *face-centered*, *end-centered*, or *body-centered* cell.
Cells in which all the points are at corners form *primitive* lattices,
the others, *centered* lattices. Nevertheless, even including these
centered lattices, there are no more than fourteen possible space
lattices. These were first enumerated by Bravais in 1848 and are
called the *fourteen Bravais lattices*. They are included in Table 1.1.

A lattice is a regular array of points in space. If at each of
these points we place an atom or some group of atoms, such as a
molecule, we obtain a *crystal structure*. Thus all crystal structures

are said to be *based on* one or another of the fourteen Bravais lattices.

A space lattice can be made up of unit cells which pack together to fill all space. In just the same way we can imagine that a crystal structure is made up of unit cells. If we know the arrangement of atoms, ions, or molecules within the unit cell, we have complete data concerning the crystal structure.

The unit cell provides a convenient way to designate the exact location of the center of mass of each atom or ion within a crystal structure. The lengths of the edges of the unit cell (a, b, c) are taken as unit lengths, and the position of any point in the cell is designated as $(u = x/a, v = y/b, w = z/c)$. For example, in the cubic unit cell, the body-centered position would be $(\frac{1}{2} \frac{1}{2} \frac{1}{2})$, a face-centered position $(\frac{1}{2} 0 \frac{1}{2})$, and so on. A perfectly general position would be (uvw).

In terms of the unit cell dimensions we can write down formulas for the distance between sets of planes *hkl*. In the cubic system the formula is

$$d_{hkl} = \frac{a_0}{(h^2 + k^2 + l^2)^{1/2}} \tag{1.1}$$

where a_0 is the edge of the unit cell.[3] For example, the distance between the 111 planes in rock salt is $d_{111} = a_0/3^{1/2} = 5.629/1.732 = 3.250$ Å.

1.7   X RAYS AND CRYSTAL STRUCTURE

Although it was quite clear that atoms in crystals must be arranged in ordered three-dimensional arrays, it was not possible to discover the form of these arrays until after the discovery of

---

[3] This result follows at once from theorems of analytic geometry. The equation of the plane *hkl* is $hx + ky + lz = a_0$. The distance from any point $(x_1 y_1 z_1)$ to this plane is

$$d = \left| \frac{hx_1 + ky_1 + lz_1 - a_0}{(h^2 + k^2 + l^2)^{1/2}} \right|$$

Hence when the point is at origin $(0, 0, 0)$ we find $d = a_0/(h^2 + k^2 + l^2)^{1/2}$.

x rays by Roentgen in 1895. Trying to see a crystal structure with ordinary light waves would be like trying to sort grains of sand with a steam shovel. The x-ray tube provided electromagnetic radiation with a wavelength about the same as atomic dimensions. A typical atom might have a hard-sphere diameter of about 2 Å. The characteristic x rays from copper, much used in x-ray crystallography, have wavelength $\lambda = 1.537$ Å. When such x rays pass through a crystal they will be diffracted and form an interference pattern, just as visible light is diffracted by a grating in which the spacings are comparable to its wavelength.

In an x-ray beam the oscillating electric and magnetic fields are directed normal to each other and to the direction of propagation of the radiation. The scattering of x rays is due mainly to the interaction between the electric field of the x rays and the negatively charged electrons in the crystal structure. Since crystal structures are based on regular lattices, we should expect them to behave as three-dimensional diffraction gratings, that is, regular arrays of scattering centers. X rays traversing crystal structures thus should give diffraction patterns.

The first work in x-ray crystallography was done by von Laue in Munich in 1912, but the first applications to crystal structure were made by W. L. Bragg in Cambridge in 1913.[4] Bragg gave a simple theory for diffraction of x rays of a single wavelength, called *monochromatic x rays*, by a crystal structure.

Consider a beam of x rays of wavelength λ incident upon a crystal face. Suppose that the crystal face consists of a regular array of atoms located at lattice points. The electric field of the x-ray beam will interact with electrons in the shells of these atoms, and as a consequence spherical waves will be scattered from each atom as a center. For the most part the scattered x rays do not form coherent beams, since they destroy each other by destructive interferences.

To understand this situation and to find out the direction of the diffracted beam we must first consider x-ray scattering by a

---

[4] The fascinating history of the discovery of x-ray diffraction and its application to crystallography is recounted by P. P. Ewald (2). This same volume contains a short autobiography by Max von Laue, which should not be missed.

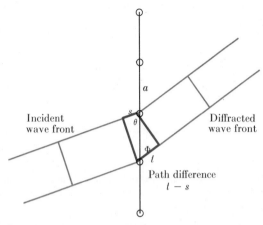

Fig. 1.4.   Diffraction of a beam of x rays by a row of scattering centers.

single line of scattering centers.   This situation is shown in Fig. 1.4.   The condition that waves scattered from two adjacent points be in phase is that their path difference equals an integral number of wavelengths.   From the figure, therefore, the path difference is

$$t - s = a \cos \Phi - a \cos \theta = n\lambda \qquad (1.2)$$

When $n = 0$, we have the zero-order diffracted rays, for which $\theta = \Phi$, that is, they form a cone generated by the original direction of incidence.   It is important to note that the direction of this cone depends only on the incident direction of the incoming beam.   It is completely independent of the spacing of the scattering centers. The higher-order diffracted beams are also cones, but their positions depend on the spacing of the scattering centers.

Now consider a beam incident on a regular pattern of points in a plane (Fig. 5.1).   The planar pattern can be made up of parallel rows of points in many different ways.   One line of points *BOD* will be directly under the beam so that $\angle ABO = \angle ABC = 90°$.   The zero-order diffracted beam from this line will be a cone with semi-vertical angle θ equal to the incident angle.   This is the same result just shown in the previous paragraph for diffraction from a set of

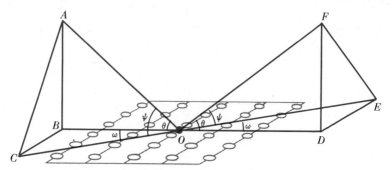

Fig. 1.5.   Zero-order diffraction by a planar array of scattering centers is geometrically equivalent to "reflection" of the incident beam.

points on a line. Consider next the scattering from *any other row* of points, for example *COE*. These would give a zero-order cone with semivertical angle ψ. We wish to find the direction of the line of intersection of the two diffraction cones. We do this by completing the solid figures *ABCO* and *FDEO*. The solid figures have three corresponding angles θ, ψ, ω equal. Hence the solid figures are similar and $\angle FDE = \angle ABC = 90°$. Therefore *OF* lies in the plane *AOB*. Since there was nothing special about the second row of points, we thus have the rather remarkable result that for the zero-order diffracted beam the angle of diffraction equals the angle of incidence. It is just as if the x-ray beam was *reflected* from the array of scattering centers in the plane. The particular spacing of these points has not a thing to do with the result, but they must be in a regular arrangement. A random (or amorphous) set of scattering points would give diffuse scattering.[5] As soon as Bragg recognized this basic fact about x-ray scattering he was able to give a simple discussion of diffraction from a three-dimensional crystal structure: The complex phenomena of x-ray diffraction were

---

[5] Note that this "reflection" of x rays is entirely different from the reflection of ordinary light by a polished surface. Optical reflection is a property due to change in velocity of light at an interface. It does not require a regular atomic arrangement at the interface. I am indebted to Dr. C. W. Bunn (3) for the derivation in Fig. 1.5.

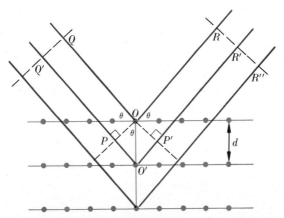

Fig. 1.6.   Derivation of Bragg diffraction condition for x-ray scattering from a set of crystal planes.

reduced to the simple geometrical problem of apparent "reflections" of x rays from crystal planes.

1.8   THE BRAGG TREATMENT

Consider in Fig. 1.6 a set of planes with spacing d and a beam of x rays of wavelength λ incident at an angle θ.   The colored lines indicate the direction of the normals to the advancing wave front. Some of the x rays are "reflected" from the topmost plane, some from the second plane, some from the third, etc.   If we are to observe the "reflected" x rays at a wave front RR'', the waves reflected from successive layers of the crystal must arrive in phase with one another.   The condition for this is that the difference in lengths of their paths be an integral number n of wavelengths. For example, $QOR - Q'O'R' = n\lambda$.   From the figure, therefore:

$$PO' + O'P' = n\lambda$$

But

$$PO' = O'P' = d \sin \theta$$

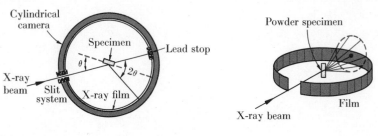

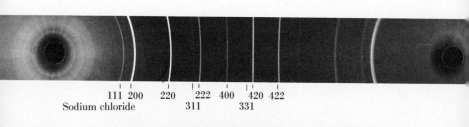

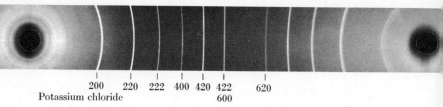

111 200   220   222 400   420 422
                    311   331
Sodium chloride

200   220 222 400 420 422   620
                            600
Potassium chloride

(b)

Fig. 1.7.   The powder method of x-ray diffraction.

Hence, we obtain the *Bragg condition*

$$n\lambda = 2d \sin \theta \qquad (1.3)$$

1.9   DETERMINATION OF THE STRUCTURE OF ROCK SALT

The clue to the structure of NaCl was found by comparing its x-ray diffraction pattern with that from KCl.   NaCl and KCl are so similar in properties that they can dissolve in each other even in the solid state, to form a continuous series of solid solutions above 500°C. This behavior was a compelling reason to believe that their crystal structures must be identical.

The crystals were set up so that they could be rotated in an x-ray beam and the angles of the principal diffraction maxima observed. Although the original work was done with single crystals, we shall use some more recent data from powdered crystals to elucidate the structures.

The principle of the powder diffraction method is shown in Fig. 1.7a. Instead of a single crystal with a face (hkl) at a definite angle θ to the x-ray beam, a mass of finely divided crystals is placed in the beam. There are so many little crystals in the sample that for any particular set of planes $\{hkl\}$ which meets the Bragg condition, $\lambda = 2d_{hkl} \sin \theta_{hkl}$, there is always a properly oriented set of crystals. The direction of the Bragg "reflected" beam is determined only by the angle θ_{hkl}. Thus for each set of planes $\{hkl\}$ the "reflected" x rays form a cone of radiation. If a flat plate is used in the camera, the resultant picture will be a series of rings. If a cylindrical film is used, we obtain pictures like those shown in Fig. 1.7b.

We *index* the pictures by measuring the distance X of each line from the central spot. Then, if D is the diameter of the camera,

$$\frac{X}{\pi D} = \frac{2\theta}{360°} \tag{1.4}$$

Hence, we obtain the Bragg angle θ corresponding to each line of the powder picture. From $\lambda = 2d \sin \theta$, $d_{hkl} = (\lambda/2)/\sin \theta$, and we calculate the spacing for each set of reflecting planes hkl. To *index the lines*, that is, to assign each one to the proper set of indices hkl, we compare these experimental spacings with the theoretical spacings, from Eq. (1.1). Of course, in order to do this, we must know the value of a_0, but this can readily be found by fitting two or three experimental d_{hkl} to the theoretical formula.

We know that NaCl and KCl must have structures based on one of the cubic lattices—simple cubic, face-centered cubic, or body-centered cubic. We believe they must have identical crystal structures, yet the x-ray diffraction picture from NaCl contains more lines than that for KCl. In fact NaCl has the lines expected for a face-centered cubic structure, whereas KCl has only those for a simple-cubic structure. The answer to this paradox becomes evident as soon as you remember that the K^+ ion and the Cl^- ion both have an argon-like structure with 18 electrons. Since the electrons are the x-ray scattering centers, a K^+ ion and a Cl^- ion have almost the same scattering power. We therefore conclude that both structures are based on a face-centered cubic lattice, but the KCl structure appears to be simple cubic because the K^+ and Cl^- ions are hardly differentiated by x rays.

A unit cell of the structure is shown in Fig. 1.8. We can describe the structure in two ways. (1) Consider a face-centered cubic lattice with lattice points at the positions of the Na^+ ions. Then place, at each lattice point, a pair of Na^+—Cl^- ions with the Na^+ to Cl^- distance $\frac{1}{2}a_0$ (between centers). (2) Consider two interpenetrating face-centered cubic lattices with the origin of one displaced by $\frac{1}{2}a_0$ along the x axis with respect to the origin of the other. Then place Na^+ ions on the points of one of these lattices and Cl^- ions on the points of the other.

We index the x-ray pictures as shown in Fig. 1.7b with $a_0 = 5.629$ Å for NaCl and 6.278 Å for KCl. There are $Z = 4$ units of NaCl per unit cell. We can use this figure to calculate an accurate

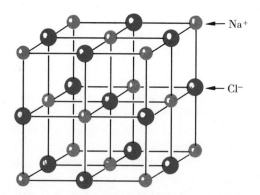

Fig. 1.8.   Unit cell of the NaCl structure.

density for the crystal. The volume of the cell $V = (a_0)^3 = (5.629)^3 \times 10^{-24} = 178.4 \times 10^{-24}$ cm³. Hence, the density,[6]

$$\rho = \frac{4(M/L)}{V} = \frac{4(58.45/6.02 \times 10^{23})}{178.4 \times 10^{-24}} = 2.177 \text{ g cm}^{-3}$$

If we did not know a_0, we could calculate it from a density determined by some other method.

1.10 HOW THE ROCK SALT STRUCTURE IS HELD TOGETHER

Sodium chloride is a typical ionic crystal. The structure is held together by electrostatic attractions between positive and negative ions. In the ordered crystal structure, electrostatic attractions between opposite charges outweigh the repulsions between ions of like charge.

The attraction between a singly charged positive ion and a singly charged negative ion in a vacuum yields an electrostatic potential energy,

$$U = \frac{-e^2}{r} \tag{1.5}$$

where e is the charge of an electron (4.80×10^{-10} statcoulomb) and r is the distance between the ions. This electrostatic, or *Coulombic* potential energy as it is sometimes called, falls off rather gradually with increasing distance between ions. If ions were simply point charges, the Coulombic energy would go toward negative infinity ($-\infty$) as a pair of ions of opposite charge came closer and closer together, but before this could happen we would begin to get repulsion between the outer electron shells of the two ions and between the positively charged nuclei. The repulsive potential energy becomes appreciable at quite small distances between the ionic centers, but falls off much more rapidly with distance than does the Coulombic attraction. The repulsive potential energy can be represented in several ways. A popular expression has been

$$U = \frac{A}{r^n} \tag{1.6}$$

---

[6] M is the formula weight and L is the Avogadro number.

where n is some number of the order of 9 to 12, and A is a constant. An expression with a better theoretical basis was given by Born and Mayer as

$$U = B \exp(-r/c) \tag{1.7}$$

where B and c are constants for a given pair of ions.

The net potential energy between two ions is the sum of the attractive term and the repulsive term,

$$U = \frac{-e^2}{r} + B \exp(-r/c) \tag{1.8}$$

For NaCl, $B = 3.0 \times 10^{-9}$ and $c = 3.3 \times 10^{-8}$, when r is in cm and the energy in ergs. (You should plot this curve for yourself from these data.) This formula represents the interaction energy in the gaseous state of one sodium ion and one chloride ion, and the minimum in the potential represents the stable equilibrium in a molecule of NaCl.

In order to calculate the electrostatic interaction energy in an entire crystal, we must start with a single ion as a center and calculate its electrostatic interaction with all other ions in the crystal. As far as the attractive potential is concerned, this calculation requires a summation over many different ions out to quite large distances from the center. As far as the repulsive potential is concerned, however, it usually suffices to consider only nearest neighbors of the central ion, since repulsive energy falls off so rapidly with distance.

Let us, first of all, consider the computation of the total electrostatic attractive energy. We start by taking the attractive term due to nearest neighbors, the repulsion due to next nearest neighbors, the attraction due to third nearest neighbors, and so on *ad infinitum*. The distance r_j from the central ion to any other ion j in a surrounding shell can be expressed in terms of the nearest neighbor distance r_0 in the crystal structure:

$$r_j = p_j r_0$$

The total electrostatic energy would thus be

$$-E_M = \sum_i \frac{\pm e^2}{r_j} = \frac{-e^2}{r_0} \sum_i (\mp) \, p_i^{-1} = \frac{-\alpha e^2}{r_0} \tag{1.9}$$

This energy is called the *Madelung energy* and the constant α is called the *Madelung constant*, after the inventor of the treatment. You must understand that if the central ion is positive, the terms in the summation are positive for negative ions j, and negative for positive ions j.

The six Cl^- ions at r_0 from the Na^+ ion (therefore $p_1 = 1$) contribute a term $6/1$ to the summation. Then there are twelve Na^+ ions at $p_2 = 2^{1/2}$ giving a term $-12/2^{1/2}$. Next, we find eight Cl^- ions at $p_3 = 3^{1/2}$, giving a contribution $8/3^{1/2}$, and so on. Thus, we can write the first few terms of the summation as

$$\alpha = \frac{6}{1} - \frac{12}{2^{1/2}} + \frac{8}{3^{1/2}} - \frac{6}{2} + \text{etc.}$$
$$= 6.000 - 8.484 + 4.620 - 3.000 + \text{etc.}$$

This series is converging slowly but presents no problems to a modern computer. Madelung made the first summation by a clever method of grouping $+$ and $-$ terms to obtain $\alpha = 1.7476$. The Madelung constants for a number of different crystal structures are given in Table 1.2.

The repulsive term has a very short range compared with the Coulombic forces and it can be obtained by summing Eq. (1.7) over only the six nearest neighbor ions.[7] We thus obtain a theoretical expression for the crystal energy of the NaCl structure,

$$E_c = \frac{-\alpha e^2}{r_0} + 6B \exp(-r_0/c) \tag{1.10}$$

At equilibrium the repulsive energy usually amounts to only about 10% of the Madelung energy.

You should note that the Madelung constant is a function of the crystal structure and can be used for all crystals of a given structure. We simply introduce the distance of closest approach r_0 characteristic of the particular substance. For example, in KCl, $r_0 = 3.14$ Å and the electrostatic contribution to its crystal energy is

---

[7] For a more exact calculation, next nearest neighbors should also be included.

**Table 1.2   Madelung Con-
stants Based on r_0, Nearest
Cation-Anion Distance**[a]

Crystal Structure	α
NaCl	1.7476
CsCl	1.7627
Zincblende(ZnS)	1.6381
Wurtzite(ZnS)	1.641
Fluorite(CaF_2)	5.0388
Rutile(TiO_2)	4.816
Corundum(Al_2O_3)	25.0312

[a] Note that α is a dimension-less number.

$$-E_M = \frac{\alpha e^2}{r_0} = \frac{(1.7476)(4.803 \times 10^{-10} \text{ statcoulomb})^2}{3.14 \times 10^{-8} \text{ cm}}$$
$$= 12.84 \times 10^{-12} \text{ erg/ion pair}$$

To obtain the value per mole we multiply by the Avogadro number. Per mole, $-E_M = (6.02 \times 10^{23})(12.84 \times 10^{-12}) = 77.33 \times 10^{11}$ erg = 185 kcal. For NaCl, $-E_M = 206$ kcal mole^{-1}, reflecting a greater electrostatic binding due to the smaller size of the Na^+ ion.

In case the ions bear more than a single charge we must use an appropriate factor in the crystal energy. For example, MgO has the same crystal structure as NaCl but the ions are $+2$ and -2 charged. Therefore, the Madelung energy would be given by $E_M = -4\alpha e^2/r_0$, and with $r_0 = 2.10$ Å we obtain $-E_M = 1105$ kcal mole^{-1}. The effect of multiple ionic charges is to increase greatly the Madelung energy of crystals—we have here the explanation of the great strength of many oxide crystals. For example, crystalline thorium oxide ThO_2, with Th^{4+} and O^{2-} ions, has the enormous Madelung energy of 5520 kcal mole^{-1}.

1.11 CRYSTAL ENERGIES

We have so far neglected a fairly important contribution to the total crystal energy. The ion Na^+ is like a neon atom, and Cl^- is like an argon atom, except for their net charges. We know that at low enough temperatures even these inert gases condense to liquids and freeze to solids. The intermolecular attractions between such neutral atoms and molecules are called *van der Waals* or *London forces*. Many organic crystals are held together entirely by such forces. In the case of interactions of ions like Na^+ and Cl^-, the London forces are still important even if overshadowed by the much larger electrostatic interaction. In Table 1.3 we list a few of the alkali halides with the calculated contributions from each of the three sources of crystal energy we have mentioned so far: Madelung energy, repulsive energy, and London energy. We see that the London energies are by no means negligible and, in fact, may approach the magnitude of the repulsive energies.

Experimental values for crystal energies are also included in Table 1.3. These can be obtained by a well-known thermochemi-

Table 1.3 Contributions to Crystal Energies of Alkali Halides (kcal mole^{-1})

Crystal	Madelung	Repulsive	London	Total	Exptl.[a] Born-Haber
LiF	285.5	−44.1	3.9	245.3	244.0
NaF	248.1	−35.3	4.5	217.3	217.9
NaCl	204.3	−23.5	5.2	186.0	182.1
NaBr	192.9	−20.6	5.5	177.8	173.1
NaI	178.0	−17.1	6.3	167.2	162.0
KCl	183.2	−21.5	7.1	168.8	165.8
RbCl	175.8	−19.9	7.9	163.8	160.1
CsCl	162.5	−17.7	11.7	156.5	149.9

[a] The zero-point vibrational energies have been included in these values.

cal method called the *Born-Haber cycle*, provided we know the standard enthalpy of formation $\Delta H_f°$ of the crystalline compound and other thermochemical quantities. The cycle goes as follows:

$Na(c) + \frac{1}{2}Cl_2(g) \rightarrow NaCl(c)$ $\Delta H_f°$ (standard enthalpy of for-
                                                              mation)

$Na(g) \rightarrow Na(c)$ $-\Delta H_s°$ (sublimation enthalpy)

$Cl(g) \rightarrow \frac{1}{2}Cl_2(g)$ $-\frac{1}{2}D_0$ (heat of dissociation per
                                                         atom)

$Na^+(g) + e^- \rightarrow Na(g)$ $-I$ (ionization energy)

$Cl^-(g) \rightarrow Cl(g) + e^-$ A (electron affinity)

$Na^+(g) + Cl^-(g) \rightarrow NaCl(c)$ $-E_c$

Therefore,

$$-E_c = \Delta H_f° - \Delta H_s° - \frac{1}{2}D_0 - I + A \qquad (1.11)$$

It would be nice to be able to say that the theory of crystal energy as outlined now allows us to predict the particular crystal structure which a substance must have in its most stable state. We then could predict, for example, why cesium chloride has a different structure from sodium chloride. However, the net energy differences between possible alternative crystal structures are usually quite small (10 kcal or so) and the theoretical calculations of the energy terms are often not sufficiently precise to pick out with certainty the most stable structure. Thus the Madelung energy of sodium chloride in a cesium chloride type structure would be only 2.0 kcal higher than in the actual structure, supposing that the same interionic distance was maintained.

1.12 VIBRATIONAL ENERGY AND
INFRARED SPECTRUM OF ROCK SALT

So far we have considered NaCl as a static structure, yet we know that the ions must have a vibrational motion even at absolute zero. This vibrational motion is responsible for the heat capacity of the solid. If the volume of a system is kept constant, its heat capacity is defined as the rate or increase of energy with increase in temperature (4):

$$C_V = \left(\frac{\partial E}{\partial T}\right)_V \qquad (1.12)$$

As temperature increases, vibrational energy increases. Particles in a crystal usually have no translational energy. Sometimes they can tumble about and thus take up rotational energy, but this is not possible in the NaCl structure, which is made up of monatomic ions which cannot take up any rotational energy. Thus all the energy taken up by the stationary crystal goes into vibrational degrees of freedom. Since there are $2L$ ions in one mole of NaCl (where $L = 6.02 \times 10^{23}$, the Avogadro number), there are $3(2L - 1) \cong 6L$ vibrational degrees of freedom. At a sufficiently high temperature each vibrational degree of freedom should have an average energy kT ($\frac{1}{2}kT$ for kinetic and $\frac{1}{2}kT$ for potential energy). The total vibrational energy would then be $E = 6LkT$ and the heat capacity per mole, $C_V = (\partial E/\partial T)_V = 6Lk = 6R \cong 11.90$ calories degree^{-1}.

The average energy of kT per vibration follows from the principle of equipartition of energy, which can be derived from classical mechanics. Actually, as Planck discovered in 1901, a vibrating system can take up energy only in quanta, the size of which is proportional to the vibration frequency ν, so that $E = h\nu$, where $h = 6.61 \times 10^{-27}$ erg sec is the Planck constant. The chance that a vibrator can acquire an energy $h\nu$ will be proportional to a factor $e^{-h\nu/kT}$. At lower temperatures, therefore, the average energy of a vibration will fall below the classical value of kT, since the size of the quantum $h\nu$ will become large relative to kT and the probability factor $e^{-h\nu/kT}$ will therefore decrease. As a consequence of the fact that vibrational energy occurs in quanta $h\nu$, vibrations of higher frequency acquire relatively less energy and the average energy of all the vibrations must be less. The heat capacity of NaCl as a function of temperature is shown in Fig. 1.9 and we see that at room temperature C_V already approaches its limiting value so that almost all vibrational degrees of freedom must then be active. At lower temperatures, however, the $C_V \to 0$ as $T \to 0$ and vibrations of successively lower frequencies fail to become excited.

We recall from the study of molecules that many molecular vibrations can be excited by absorption of radiation of appropriate

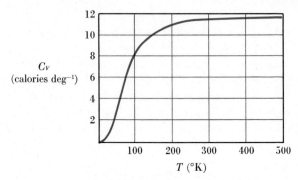

C_V
(calories deg^{-1})

Fig. 1.9.   Heat capacity of NaCl as function of temperature.

wavelength, usually in the infrared (IR). The requirement for a molecular vibration to be active in the IR is that it result in an oscillating dipole moment. Since every pair of Na$^+$ and Cl$^-$ ions is in effect a strong dipole, we can therefore expect vibrations in rock salt to be excited by absorption of infrared radiation. The absorption spectrum of a pure crystal of NaCl in the infrared region is shown in Fig. 1.10a. We see that there is a strong band with maximum absorption at 61 microns.[8] Figure 1.10b shows the onset of IR absorption (the short wavelength limit of the band) in several crystals having the NaCl structure. We notice that the heavier the ions, the longer the wavelength of the IR band, and hence the lower the frequency at which infrared absorption occurs. We can understand this result simply in terms of the effect of mass on the frequency of a harmonic oscillator with force constant β, given by the equation,

$$\nu = \frac{1}{2\pi} \left(\frac{\beta}{\mu} \right)^{1/2} \tag{1.13}$$

Here μ is the reduced mass $(1/\mu = 1/m_1 + 1/m_2)$.

Evidently, if we wish to get good transmission in the infrared region we must use a crystal in which the ions are as heavy as pos-

[8] This corresponds to a photon energy of about 0.02 eV.

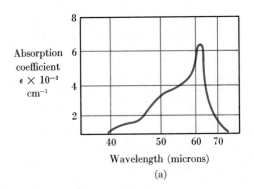

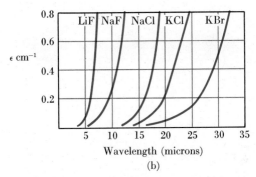

Fig. 1.10. **Infrared absorption spectra: (a) The absorption band in NaCl. (b) The onset of absorption in various alkali halides.**

sible. A solid solution of thallium bromide and thallium iodide known as KRS-5 has been grown especially for infrared windows. The reason why pure thallium iodide cannot be used is that it has a hexagonal structure and hence would not give isotropic windows. The solid solution KRS-5 with 42 atom % TlBr, 58 atom % TlI, has a cubic structure.

In addition to being good transmitters of electromagnetic radiation of certain wavelengths, crystals in general are good conductors of sound. In a gas, sound travels as a longitudinal wave of compression. In a solid we can have sound waves carried by vibration of the ions or atoms. Thus the vibrations of NaCl can be divided into two groups, *acoustical vibrations* which behave like sound waves and are therefore collectively called *phonons* in the crystal, and *optical vibrations* which behave like light waves and are called *optical phonons*. The basic distinction is that acoustical vibrations do not cause an oscillating electric field—they are mechanical but not electrical vibrations. In a solid, however, both acoustical and optical vibrations can be either transverse or longitudinal.

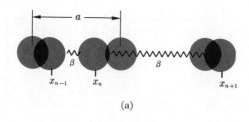

(a)

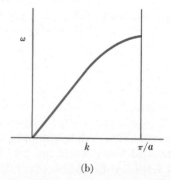

(b)

Fig. 1.11. (a) One-dimensional model for vibrations in a monatomic linear array. (b) Dispersion curve: frequency versus wave number for Born model.

1.13 VIBRATIONS IN A MONATOMIC SOLID

Before we discuss in the next section the vibrations of a one-dimensional lattice with two different masses on alternate sites, we shall discuss the case in which each site is occupied by an identical atom of mass m. This case would be a one-dimensional model for an element, whereas with two different masses we would have a model for a compound. The situation is shown in Fig. 1.11a. The coordinate of the atom located at site n is designated x_n. As the atom vibrates about its equilibrium point, it is subject to two restoring forces, one proportional to its distance from the atom on the right $(x_n - x_{n+1})$ and the other to its distance from the atom on the left $(x_n - x_{n-1})$. With the restoring force constant β, the equation of motion (force = mass $\times$ acceleration) becomes

$$m \frac{d^2 x_n}{dt^2} = -\beta(2x_n - x_{n+1} - x_{n-1}) \tag{1.14}$$

A reasonable trial solution for this equation would be a wave motion along the line with a frequency $\nu = \omega/2\pi$ and a wavelength $\lambda = 2\pi/\mathbf{k}$. Instead of a continuous coordinate x we introduce na, where a is the lattice spacing. Thus the trial solution would be

$$x_n = A e^{2\pi i(\nu t + na/\lambda)} = A e^{i(\omega t + n\mathbf{k}a)}$$

where A is an amplitude. We take the second derivative of this solution and substitute it back into the Eq. (1.14),

$$m \frac{d^2 x_n}{dt^2} = -mA\omega^2 e^{i(\omega t + n\mathbf{k}a)} = -\beta(2A e^{i(\omega t + n\mathbf{k}a)} - A e^{i(\omega t + (n+1)\mathbf{k}a)} - A e^{i(\omega t + (n-1)\mathbf{k}a)})$$

whence

$$\omega^2 = \frac{2\beta}{m}\left(1 - \frac{e^{i\mathbf{k}a} + e^{-i\mathbf{k}a}}{2}\right) = \frac{2\beta}{m}(1 - \cos \mathbf{k}a)$$

$$\omega^2 = \frac{2\beta}{m}\left(2 \sin^2 \frac{\mathbf{k}a}{2}\right)$$

We thus obtain a relation between frequency and wave number

$$\omega = \left(\frac{\beta}{m}\right)^{1/2} 2 \sin \frac{\mathbf{k}a}{2} \tag{1.15}$$

This is a most interesting and important relation and deserves some contemplation and study. We have plotted it in Fig. 1.11b. Since the values of the sine are restricted to the range from 0 to $+1$, it follows that the values of $ka/2$ are restricted to the range from 0 to $+\pi/2$, or $\mathbf{k}$ itself is restricted to the range 0 to $+\pi/a$. The largest value of $\mathbf{k}(= +\pi/a)$ corresponds to the smallest allowed wavelength for waves in the one-dimensional lattice, which would be $2a$, twice the lattice distance.

1.14 SIMPLE MODEL FOR VIBRATIONS IN AN IONIC CRYSTAL

With the monatomic case as a guide, we can now discuss a one-dimensional model for the vibrations of an ionic crystal, due originally to Max Born. It consists of a linear diatomic structure containing two masses m_1 and m_2 alternating along a line and connected by springs with the same force constant β. Since motion is restricted to a line, we consider only longitudinal waves, in which the direction of propagation is the same as direction of vibration. Mass m_1 will occur on lattice sites labeled $2n(0, 2, 4, \ldots)$ and m_2 on sites $2n + 1(1, 3, 5, \ldots)$. We write down the Newtonian equations of motion: force = mass $\times$ acceleration. The coordinate of an atom on site $2n$ will be denoted by x_{2n} and its acceleration by $\ddot{x}_{2n}$ which means d^2x_{2n}/dt^2. By Hooke's law the restoring force on an atom is proportional to the compression or expansion of the spring $(f = -\beta x)$, and the net change x in the interatomic spacings is $[(x_{2n+1} - x_{2n}) + (x_{2n-1} - x_{2n})]$. Thus we have equations of motion as follows:

$$m_1\ddot{x}_{2n} = \beta(x_{2n+1} + x_{2n-1} - 2x_{2n})$$
$$m_2\ddot{x}_{2n+1} = \beta(x_{2n+2} + x_{2n} - 2x_{2n+1}) \tag{1.16}$$

We want solutions which are traveling waves of frequency $\omega(= 2\pi\nu)$. The frequency is related to the velocity v_0 of the wave by

$$\nu = \frac{v_0}{\lambda} \tag{1.17}$$

where λ is the wavelength. The *wave number*, as before, is

$$\mathbf{k} = \frac{2\pi}{\lambda} \tag{1.18}$$

The solutions will have the form

$$\begin{aligned} x_{2n} &= A e^{i(\omega t + 2n\mathbf{k}a)} \\ x_{2n+1} &= B e^{i(\omega t + (2n+1)\mathbf{k}a)} \end{aligned} \tag{1.19}$$

To obtain the allowed values of the vibrational amplitudes A and B, we substitute these solutions back into the equations of motion, to obtain

$$\begin{aligned} -\omega^2 A m_1 &= \beta(2B \cos \mathbf{k}a - 2A) \\ -\omega^2 B m_2 &= \beta(2A \cos \mathbf{k}a - 2B) \end{aligned} \tag{1.20}$$

In order for these homogeneous equations to have nontrivial roots, the determinant of the coefficients must vanish (5).

$$\begin{vmatrix} 2\beta - m_1\omega^2 & -2\beta \cos \mathbf{k}a \\ \\ -2\beta \cos \mathbf{k}a & 2\beta - m_2\omega^2 \end{vmatrix} = 0 \tag{1.21}$$

We multiply out the determinant and solve the quadratic equation for ω^2, to obtain

$$\omega^2 = \beta\mu^{-1} \pm \beta\left[\mu^{-2} - \frac{4\sin^2 \mathbf{k}a}{m_1 m_2}\right]^{1/2} \tag{1.22}$$

where μ is the reduced mass.

We use only the positive values of ω and find on plotting that the curves ω versus $\mathbf{k}$ fall into branches as shown in Fig. 1.12. Such a curve of frequency versus wave number is called a *dispersion curve*.[9] We can see the difference between the solutions in these two branches by considering a limiting case. As $\mathbf{k}$ goes to 0, we find for the higher-frequency branch that A/B goes to m_2/m_1 and ω goes to $(2\beta/\mu)^{1/2}$. On the other hand, for the lower-frequency

---

[9] You may be more familiar with the dispersion curve as a plot of index of refraction n versus wavelength. Since $n = c/v$, ratio of speed of light in vacuum to speed in a medium, you can see, however, that a $\mathbf{k}$ versus ω plot gives the same information (6).

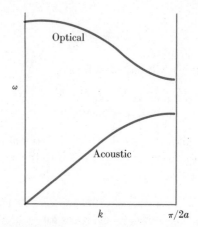

Fig. 1.12. Vibration frequencies of diatomic linear array as given by the Born model.

branch, A/B goes to 1 and ω goes to 0. Thus the upper branch corresponds to the atoms of different mass vibrating exactly out of phase, whereas in the lower branch they are exactly in phase. The upper branch is therefore called the *optical branch* and the lower branch is called the *acoustic branch* of the vibrational spectrum. If the atoms m_1 and m_2 have opposite charges like Na^+ and Cl^-, vibrations of the optical branch will be associated with an oscillating electric dipole in the crystal, as the oppositely charged ions move with opposite phase to each other. Hence such vibrations can be excited by the oscillating electric fields of visible, ultraviolet, or infrared light, depending on their characteristic frequencies. On the other hand, vibrations of the acoustic branch cannot be excited by the electric fields of light waves, but they can be excited mechanically or by sound waves. In an actual three-dimensional crystal the theory of lattice vibrations is complicated by the fact that transverse vibrational modes (with both acoustic and optical branches) exist, as well as the longitudinal modes we described in the one-dimensional case. In the transverse modes, the direction of vibration is normal to the direction of propagation.

1.15 POINT DEFECTS IN ALKALI HALIDES

So far we have been discussing perfect salt crystals, in which every Na^+ ion and Cl^- ion is on its proper lattice site. Yet the second law of thermodynamics tells us that nothing perfect can exist at equilibrium. A certain randomness or disorder (measured by the entropy S) is always present, so that the equilibrium condition is at the minimum of the Gibbs function, $G = H - TS$. At any temperature above absolute zero, which we cannot reach anyway, the system must have some disorder (entropy).

What kind of disorder can exist in the structure of a crystal such as NaCl? Disorder localized at definite lattice sites is called a *point defect* in the crystal structure. The German Schottky in 1930 and the Russian Frenkel in 1926 pointed out two simple kinds of point defects. The Schottky defect consists of a pair of vacant sites, one at an Na^+ site and one at a Cl^- site. Thus the electrical neutrality of the crystal is preserved. Usually the vacancy pair is separated (dissociated). There is more entropy of disorder in that way, but sometimes associated double vacancies will occur. The Frenkel defect consists of an ion in an interstitial position and the vacancy it has left behind at a normal lattice site. Here also associated and dissociated defects are possible, with the latter being more common.

Frenkel and Schottky defects are called *intrinsic defects*. They do not alter the purity or stoichiometric composition of a crystal in which they occur. Actually, the Frenkel defect does not occur to an appreciable extent in NaCl crystals. The principal defects are Schottky defects. In silver chloride, on the other hand, Frenkel defects consisting of interstitial Ag^+ ions and vacant Ag^+ sites are the main kind of disorder. Yet AgCl has the same crystal structure as NaCl. The reason for their difference in defect populations is not that the Ag^+ ion is much larger than the Na^+ ion, having a crystal radius of 1.20 Å as compared to 0.96 Å for the latter, since KCl in which the ionic radius of K^+ is almost identical with that of Ag^+ also has Schottky defects. The reason for the difference between AgCl and NaCl must be in the fact that Ag^+ is a transition metal ion with an outer configuration $4d^{10}$, whereas Na^+ has an inert gas configuration of $3s^23p^6$. There will be a tendency for the $4d$ electrons of Ag^+ to occupy the empty $3d$ orbitals of the Cl^- with consequent covalent bonding. (The ionization potential of Ag is 7.54 V, and that of Na is only 5.12 V. It is much harder to take an electron away from Ag than from Na.) In an interstitial Ag^+, which is in a site of considerable compressive stress, the tendency toward covalent bonding will be enhanced.

1.16 CALCULATION OF DEFECT CONCENTRATIONS

We can calculate the equilibrium number of defects from the entropy they produce. It costs an energy E to make a defect but we gain entropy S due to the resultant disorder. Suppose n defects are distributed at random among N crystal sites. The number of ways of mixing the defects among the sites is

$$W = \frac{N!}{n!(N-n)!} \tag{1.23}$$

This is the total permutations among N sites, divided by the permutations of the n defective sites times the permutations of the $N - n$ nondefective sites.

Take the case of 10 sites and 2 defects. There are $10!/8!2! = 45$ ways of scattering the defects among the sites. In this case the answer can be checked easily, since there are 10 different places for the first defect and 9 for the second, but only $\frac{1}{2}$ the 90 arrangements are different, since the defects are indistinguishable from each other.

The randomness or degree of disorder in a system determines the thermodynamic function called the *entropy* S of the system (7). Boltzmann in 1895 demonstrated his famous relationship,

$$S = k \ln W \tag{1.24}$$

The change in G at constant temperature is

$$\Delta G = \Delta H - T\Delta S$$

Hence, from Eqs. (1.24) and (1.23), for creation of n defects,

$$\Delta G = n\Delta H - kT \ln\left[\frac{N!}{(N-n)!n!}\right] \qquad (1.25)$$

At equilibrium, at constant T, the Gibbs function of the system must be a minimum with respect to changes in the number of defects n. Thus,

$$\left(\frac{\partial \Delta G}{\partial n}\right)_T = 0 \qquad (1.26)$$

With the use of Stirling's formula for factorials,

$$\ln X! = X \ln X - X \qquad (1.27)$$

we find

$$\ln \frac{n}{N-n} = \frac{\Delta H}{kT}$$

If $n \ll N$,

$$n = Ne^{-\Delta H/kT} \qquad (1.28)$$

As an example, if ΔH is $\sim$1 eV and $T = 1000°K$, $n/N \approx 10^{-5}$. For pairs of vacancies (Schottky defects) the number of ways of forming the defect is squared and we get finally

$$n = Ne^{-\Delta H/2kT} \qquad (1.29)$$

For Frenkel defects,

$$n = (NN')^{1/2}e^{-\Delta H/2kT} \qquad (1.30)$$

when N' is the number of available interstitial sites.

It is evident that an important quantity in the theory of defects is the enthalpy of formation ΔH of a defect. We should be able to calculate this ΔH in an ionic crystal like NaCl by a method similar to that used to calculate the Madelung energy. To remove an Na^+ ion from the NaCl structure and place it on the surface will require energy approximately equal to the Madelung energy. On the other hand, the structure will relax around the vacancy thus created so that some of the energy lost in removing the ion will be regained by rearrangement of the structure in the neighborhood of the vacancy. Such calculations for NaCl give $\Delta H = 46$ kcal mole^{-1} for the formation of a Schottky defect and $\Delta H = -30$ kcal mole^{-1} for association of the pair of vacancies.

1.17   DEFECTS AND IONIC MOBILITY

If a crystal structure were perfect, with every ion exactly in its ordained place, it would be difficult for any movement of ions to take place.   When such internal migrations in crystals were studied with radioactive tracers, the experiments showed that the ions in NaCl are not locked into place.   In a typical experiment the nuclide ^{24}Na, a beta emitter with a half-life of 15 hr, was used.   A thin layer of radioactive NaCl was evaporated onto a face of an NaCl crystal.   A second crystal was placed over the active layer to prevent its loss by evaporation and the radioactive sandwich was heated for a fixed time at a controlled temperature.   The results are shown in Fig. 1.13a, in which the darkened region represents concentration of radioactive tracer.   The exact concentration is determined by taking thin sections of the crystal and counting the radioactivity in each section.   The data are plotted in Fig. 1.13b. The theoretical expression for diffusion in a case like this is

$$c = \frac{A}{2(\pi Dt)^{1/2}} \exp\left(- \frac{x^2}{4Dt}\right); \quad \ln c = \ln\left(\frac{A}{2(\pi Dt)^{1/2}}\right) - \frac{x^2}{4Dt} \quad (1.31)$$

Here A is the initial activity of the tracer layer, c is the concentration at distance x from the interface after a time t, and D is the *diffusion coefficient*.[10]   From Eq. (1.31) we see that by plotting the logarithm of the activity versus the square of the distance of penetration we should obtain a linear graph, the slope of which is $1/4Dt$. Knowing the time t of the diffusion anneal, we can thus readily calculate D.

When this experiment was repeated for NaCl over a range of temperatures, the experimental D's were found to depend on temperature in accord with the equation.

---

[10] We can define D in terms of Fick's first law of diffusion which states that the flow in the x direction of a substance through unit cross section in unit time is proportional to its concentration gradient in the x direction, so that $F = -D(\partial c/\partial x)$.

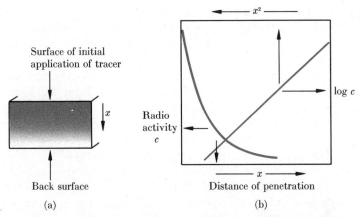

Fig. 1.13. **Determination of the diffusion coefficient of Na⁺ in NaCl crystal. (a) Radioautograph of the diffusion profile. (b) Plot of the activity versus penetration data both directly and in accord with Eq. (1.31).**

$$D = D_0 \exp\left(\frac{-E_a}{RT}\right) = 3.13 \exp\left(\frac{-41.4 \text{ kcal}}{RT}\right) \text{cm}^2 \text{ sec}^{-1}$$

This equation has the form of the Arrhenius equation which gives the temperature dependence of the rate constant for a chemical reaction (8). The activation energy for diffusion $E_a = 41.4$ kcal mole^{-1}.

The diffusion of Na⁺ in NaCl occurs by way of the vacant Na⁺ sites due to Schottky defects in the crystal. As long as there are empty sites, it is not so difficult to move the ions around. Without empty places every ion would be locked quite tightly into position.

The activation energy for diffusion of Na⁺ in NaCl is the sum of two factors, the energy required to make a vacancy in the structure and the energy required to move the Na⁺ ion from an occupied site to an empty adjacent site. Thus the apparent activation energy for diffusion should be given by

$$E_a = \frac{\Delta H_f}{2} + \Delta E^* \tag{1.32}$$

We use our previous estimation of $\Delta H_f/2 = 23$ kcal, to find $\Delta E^* = 18$. This result is typical. The overall activation energy for solid state diffusion is divided about half-and-half between the energy to make the defect and the energy to move it.

The concentration of vacancies in NaCl is fairly high at elevated temperature, about 5×10^{-5} atom fraction or 2.2×10^{17} cm^{-3} at 1000°K. When a crystal is heated and quenched rapidly back to room temperature, quite a few vacancies will be "frozen-in," to give a metastable concentration of defects which can contribute to the diffusion without being paid for again in terms of formation energy. This is the main reason why apparent activation energies for diffusion and ionic conductivity sometimes appear lower at low temperatures. In such cases ions can still move around by way of frozen-in vacancies, but the concentration of vacancies does not change much with T. Thus the apparent E_a simply equals ΔE^*.

1.18   DOPING FOR DEFECTS

There is another way, however, to inject a really appreciable concentration of vacancies into the NaCl structure: by doping the crystal with a bivalent cation such as Ca^{2+} or Mn^{2+}. Suppose we crystallize NaCl from a melt containing a few tenths percent $CaCl_2$ or $MnCl_2$. Some of the Ca^{2+} ions (0.98 Å) or Mn^{2+} (0.80 Å) are included in the crystal structure.[11] Since, however, Ca^{2+} has a charge of $+2$, how can it replace a Na^+ without destroying the electrical neutrality of the crystal, which we cannot possibly allow? The answer is obvious: by leaving one Na^+ site vacant for each Ca^{2+} built into the structure. The final result is shown in Fig. 1.14 (together with other varieties of point defects). By such doping we get a crystal with a much higher concentration of defects than a purer crystal could possibly have. You can also do a similar trick with crystals composed of multivalent ions. If you dissolve some Cl^- in ZnS, you can get some charge compensation by leaving vacant cation sites. The crystal structure into which

---

[11] The atom fraction of foreign bivalent cations in the alkali halides is usually less than 10^{-4}.

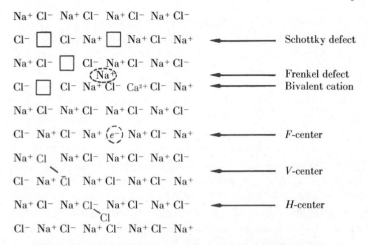

Fig. 1.14. Principal varieties of point defects in NaCl.

such defects are introduced by doping is often called the *host structure*.

Diffusion coefficients of host ions and ionic conductivity in such doped crystals are often extremely high compared to those in pure crystals. The reason is that we no longer need to pay energy to create the defects responsible for ionic mobility [ΔH_f in Eq. (1.32)]. The only activation energy term is the ΔE^* for movement of defects. The moral is that if you want atoms to move more freely in solids you must deliberately introduce defects into the social order of the ideal state.

1.19 COLOR CENTERS

If a sodium chloride crystal is heated in sodium vapor it acquires a deep yellow color. Potassium chloride heated in potassium vapor acquires a magenta color. The color centers responsible for these effects were first studied carefully by R. W. Pohl and his co-workers, who called them *F-centers* from the German *Farbenzentren*. We now recognize many color centers and restrict the

name *F-center* to the principal one caused by heating a crystal in a
vapor of its metallic constituent. When a NaCl crystal is heated
in chlorine gas it also becomes colored, and these centers are called
V-centers.

As a crystal takes up extra sodium there will be an excess of
occupied sodium sites so that we may expect to have vacant Cl⁻
sites in the crystal. A possible situation will be that shown in Fig.
1.14, a sodium atom adjacent to a vacant Cl⁻ site. There are
actually six Na⁺ ions around a vacant Cl⁻ site[12] and there is no
reason why any particular one should have the electron all to itself
and hence become a neutral atom. We believe therefore that the
electron is *delocalized* in the vacant site—we can think of it as being
in an orbit shared by all six Na⁺ ions. If ordinary NaCl crystals
without excess sodium are irradiated with x rays some *F*-centers
are formed, as electrons ejected from ions are trapped at Schottky
defects already present in the crystal.

If the concentrations of *F*-centers are so dilute that they do
not interact with one another, the number of centers can be estimated directly from the area under the absorption curve in the
optical spectrum. An equation due to Smakula gives this relation:

$$Nf = \frac{9mc}{2e^2} \frac{n}{(n^2 + 2)^2} E_M W = 1.29 \times 10^{17} \frac{n}{(n^2 + 2)^2} E_M W \qquad (1.33)$$

Here N is the number of *F*-centers per unit volume, f is the *oscillator strength* which relates to the probability for light absorption by
the center, n is the refractive index for the crystal at the wavelength of the absorption band. The absorption coefficient in cm⁻¹
at the band maximum is E_M and W is half-width of band in electron
volts.[13] The oscillator strength f is near to unity so that one can
use the Smakula equation to estimate concentrations of color
centers in crystals. The lower limit of detection would be about
10^6 cm⁻³, and the concentrations in natural and synthetic crystals
may range up to 10^{18} cm⁻³.

A lot of good evidence indicates that the *F*-center is an electron

---

[12] Only four are seen in the two-dimensional section.
[13] One electron volt (per atom or ion) is equivalent to 23.05 kcal mole⁻¹.

trapped at a vacant anion site. The best proof of the structure of the *F*-center was found in its paramagnetic resonance spectrum. An unpaired electron will have an unpaired spin and thus give an electron paramagnetic moment. The paramagnetic spectrum of the *F*-center was clearly due to a single unpaired electron. Its exact location was fixed by the hyperfine interaction of the magnetic moment due to the spin of the electron with the magnetic moments of the sodium nuclei surrounding the center.

1.20 *V*-CENTERS

If we look at the absorption spectrum of NaCl after irradiation with x rays, we find a strong *F*-center absorption band, but in addition toward the ultraviolet side, we find weaker bands. The centers responsible for these were called *V*-centers, and the elucidation of their detailed structure has led to some of the most interesting work in the solid state chemistry of alkali halides.

It was first believed that the *V*-center was an "antimorph" of the *F*-center, that is, positive charges trapped at anion vacancies in contrast to negative charges trapped at cation vacancies, Curiously, this exact antimorph has never been positively identified. In 1955 Känzig studied the electron-spin-resonance spectrum of one of the *V*-centers and was able to identify it positively as a Cl_2^- ion oriented along [110] axes of the host crystal. It is a Cl_2^- ion (covalently bonded) in a perfectly normal NaCl structure; i.e., there are no vacancies or other defects adjacent to it. The x rays must drive an electron from a Cl^- ion and the resultant Cl atom bonds to a neighboring Cl^-. The lost electron might form an *F*-center elsewhere in the crystal.

Another unusually interesting center is the *H*-center. In this case a Cl_2^- ion is crowded into a single Cl^- site and oriented so as to crowd two adjacent Cl^- ions along the [110] axis. The *H*-center is exactly *complementary* to the *F*-center. If an *H* and an *F* come together they can interact to form a perfect crystal again. And so we end this chapter exactly where we began—with a crystal of common salt.

REFERENCES

(1) W. F. de Jong, *General Crystallography* (San Francisco: Freeman, 1959).

(2) P. P. Ewald, *Fifty Years of X-Ray Diffraction* (Utrecht: International Union of Crystallography, 1962).

(3) C. W. Bunn, *Chemical Crystallography* (London and New York: Oxford University Press, 1945).

(4) B. H. Mahan, *Elementary Chemical Thermodynamics* (New York: Benjamin, 1963), p. 40.

(5) G. J. Kynch, *Mathematics for the Chemist* (New York: Academic Press, 1955), p. 304.

(6) C. Kittel, *Introduction to Solid State Physics* (New York: Wiley, 1966), p. 142.

(7) J. D. Fast, *Entropy* (New York: McGraw-Hill, 1962).

(8) E. L. King, *How Chemical Reactions Occur* (New York: Benjamin, 1963).

II

Gold

G OLD IS THE MOST perfect of all metals consisting of the most pure Mercury, most perfectly digested and ripened, by virtue of a most excellent and fixed ruddy Sulphur, wherewith it is most exactly mixed and united. Hence it comes to have a yellow color. . . . The Chymists do call it Sol, the sun." This was a theory of the metallic state as given by Daniel Sennert in 1660.

2.1 CRYSTAL STRUCTURE

Although gold may be the king of metals it has a most common crystal structure, the cubic closest-packed or face-centered cubic structure, found also in a score of other metals. If we want to pack together spheres of identical diameter so as to leave the least possi-

ble empty space, we can find two different ways to do so. We start
with a closest-packed layer (Fig. 2.1). Note the hexagonal symmetry of the packing. Each sphere has six nearest neighbors in
the plane with centers arrayed at the vertices of a regular hexagon.
There is no way to pack a layer more closely than this since no
more than six separate circles can make contact with a given circle
of the same diameter.

Notice the triangular void spaces in the closest-packed layer.
There are two sets of these triangular spaces, one with the vertices
of the triangles pointing upward and one with the vertices pointing
downward. We can call these sites B and C and the original positions of the centers of the spheres in the first layer we shall call sites
A. Now suppose we wish to place a second closest-packed layer on
top of the first layer. If we place a sphere on a B site, we cannot
also place a sphere on a neighboring C site. Therefore, we can pack
the second layer by nesting the spheres either all in B sites or all in
C sites, but not in both if we wish to maintain closest packing.
Suppose we choose therefore AB as sites for the first two layers
(Fig. 2.1). This is not really a different structure from AC, since

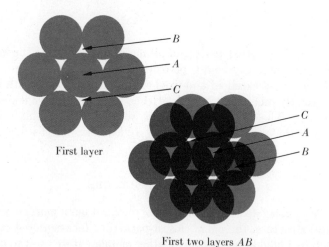

First layer

First two layers AB

Fig. 2.1. Closest-packed layers of spheres.

it can be converted into it by simple change of the coordinate system to which we refer the positions of the centers.

When we come to the third layer, however, a real choice presents itself. We can either use C sites for a closest-packed third layer, or go back and place the third layer exactly on top of the original first layer, that is, use A sites. The two possible structures that result can be designated, therefore, as ABC and ABA (Fig. 2.2). We notice that in both these structures we have ideal closest packing and any given sphere has twelve neighbors touching it, six in the same plane and three above and three below. The difference is that in the ABC structure, the triangle of three above is rotated 180° with respect to the triangle of three below, whereas in the ABA structure, the triangles above and below are oriented in exactly the same way.

These two structures were worked out about 1883 by William Barlow, then curator of the London Science Museum. He suggested them as likely structures for metals long before experimental methods were developed to determine the structures by x rays. The structure ABA can be based on a hexagonal unit cell containing two atoms ($Z = 2$) as shown in Fig. 2.2. It is called the *hexagonal closest-packed structure*. The closest-packed layers are in planes normal to the hexagonal c axis. The structure ABC can be based on a face-centered cubic unit cell and is called the *cubic closest-packed structure*. In this case the closest-packed

Table 2.1 Crystal Structures of Metals

Cubic closest-packed	Ag, Al, Au, αCa, βCo, Cu, γFe, Sr, Th, Ni, Pb, Pt
Hexagonal closest-packed	αBe, γCa, Cd, αCo, βCr, Mg, αZr, Os, αTi, Zn
Body-centered cubic	Ba, αCr, Cs, αFe, K, Li, Mo, Na, βZr, Ta, βTi, V
Simple-cubic	Po
Rhombohedral, layers	Bi, As, Sb
Body-centered tetragonal	βSn, βGe
Face-centered tetragonal	γMn, In

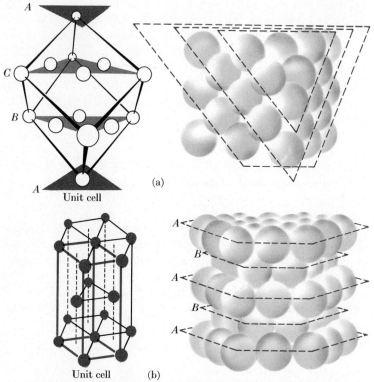

Fig. 2.2. Structures that arise from the closest packing of uniform spheres. (a) Cubic closest packing. The closest-packed layers are the 111 planes in the face-centered cubic structure. (b) Hexagonal closest packing. The closest-packed layers are the 001 planes.

layers are the 111 planes in the structure, that is, normal to the [111] direction which is the 3-fold symmetry axis of the cube. This arrangement is also shown in Fig. 2.2.

Most metals crystallize either in the cubic closest-packed structure or in the hexagonal closest-packed structure. A few, however, occur in body-centered structures. Others occur in a modified hexagonal closest-packed structure called *double hexagonal closest packing* in which the layer arrangement is *ABACABAC*, etc. Various metals with their crystal structures are summarized in Table 2.1.

2.2 THE ELECTRON GAS

The true nature of metals remained pretty much a mystery until after the discovery of the electron in 1895. The major problem had always been to explain their high electrical conductivity. Drude in 1905 suggested that a piece of metal is like a box containing a gas of freely mobile electrons. When an electric field is applied, the electrons flow along the resultant gradient of potential giving rise to an electric current. In this model the electron can be assigned a certain mean free path λ and mean free time τ between collisions. During this time τ the electron is accelerated by the field, but if it experiences a collision with another electron or with an atomic core, its velocity in the field direction will on the average be lost. We can use these ideas to develop a simple theory for the electrical conductivity of metals.

Conductivity σ is given by the ratio of current to field j/F. The term *mobility* μ refers to the velocity of a particle under a unit field strength, that is, $\mu = u/F$. Hence, conductivity in general can be written as

$$\sigma = Ne\mu \tag{2.1}$$

where N is the number of charge carriers (electrons in a metal) per unit volume, e is their charge, and μ is their mobility. The mean velocity of drift in the field direction is the product of the acceleration caused by the field and one half the time τ over which it acts. The acceleration is force divided by mass, eF/m, and hence the mean velocity of drift is $eF\tau/2m$. Hence, the mobility is $e\tau/2m$ and the conductivity becomes

$$\sigma = \frac{Ne^2\tau}{2m} \tag{2.2}$$

If the electrons behave like atoms in a perfect gas, their average kinetic energy, $\frac{1}{2}mv^2 = \frac{3}{2}kT$, where T is the absolute temperature and k the Boltzmann constant. Their mean free path is $\lambda = \tau v$. In these terms we rewrite the expression for the conductivity as

$$\sigma = \frac{Ne^2\lambda}{2mv} \quad \text{with } v = \left(\frac{3kT}{m}\right)^{1/2} \tag{2.3}$$

To see how well this formula works for gold, let us substitute the appropriate values for the various terms. We shall assume that each gold atom contributes only its $6s$ valence electron to the conductivity. At 20°:

$N = L\rho/M = 5.90 \times 10^{28}$ m^{-3}, $e = 1.60 \times 10^{-19}$ coulomb, $\lambda = 20 \times 10^{-9}$ m, $m = 9.11 \times 10^{-31}$ kg, $v = 11.6 \times 10^4$ m sec^{-1}. Hence we find $\sigma = 14.3 \times 10^7$ ohm^{-1} m^{-1}. The experimental value at 20° is $\sigma = 4.90 \times 10^7$ ohm^{-1} m^{-1}.

The difficulty in this treatment is that we have used a value for the mean free path λ without explaining how we picked it. As a matter of fact λ must be close to the value given. One of the interesting ways of finding λ experimentally is to study the conductivity of thin metallic films. If you make the film thin enough you should eventually reach a thickness which is less than the electronic mean free path. Any further attempt to thin the film should cut down the effective mean free path of the electrons and accordingly lower the conductivity. It is found experimentally that the conductivity of thin films does not depend on thickness until you get down to about 200 Å. This means that the mean free path is at least as long as this, so that the electron apparently moves through about a hundred atoms without hitting anything. Thus a serious difficulty with the classical theory is a poorly defined concept of mean free path of the electron and an inability to explain its large value.

2.3 HEAT CAPACITY PARADOX

A much more serious difficulty with the classical theory, indeed it might be called a fatal defect, is the heat capacity paradox. If electrons in a metal behave like atoms in a gas they should be able to take up translational kinetic energy when a metal is heated.

In accord with the equipartition principle this energy would amount to $\frac{3}{2}kT$ per electron or $\frac{3}{2}LkT = \frac{3}{2}RT$ per mole of electrons, where L is the Avogadro number. The electronic heat capacity $C_V = (\partial E/\partial T)_V$ would be $\frac{3}{2}R \approx 3$ cal deg^{-1} mole^{-1}. The heat capacity of gold at 20°C, as we know, is about $3R \approx 6$ cal deg^{-1} mole^{-1}, but this has already been accounted for completely by the vibrational degrees of freedom (as explained for sodium chloride on page 23). There is nothing left at all for the electronic heat capacity demanded by the electron-gas theory. Thus the electron gas explained conductivity quite well but it did not display the predicted thermodynamic properties. This failure of the theory at first seemed to be a fatal defect.

2.4 ELECTRONS AS FERMIONS

The key to this problem was found in the Pauli exclusion principle (1). All chemists are familiar with the way in which this principle restricts the arrangement of electrons in wave functions and energy levels within atoms, and hence leads to the structure of the periodic table. No two electrons in an atom can have all four quantum numbers the same. In an atomic structure these quantum numbers are n, l, m_l, m_s. Thus, in a given state specified by n, l, and m_l, we can put two electrons of opposite spins, $m_s = \pm\frac{1}{2}$. What can we say about similar restrictions on electrons not in an isolated atom but in a piece of metal?

The first solution to this problem was given by Sommerfeld in 1928. He accepted the electron-gas picture of a metal but added the requirement that the electrons must behave in accordance with the rules of quantum mechanics. The problem was therefore to find the allowed wave functions and energy states of an electron within a piece of metal. His first model was to assume that electrons moved in a potential field such as that shown in Fig. 2.3. Except at the surface of the metal, they were thus completely free, but at the surface there was a potential wall which prevented their escape from the metal. The height of this wall was designated as ϕ, the well-known *thermionic work function* of a metal.

The problem therefore is one of the earliest ones we meet in

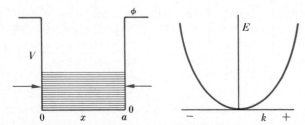

Fig. 2.3. One-dimensional potential energy well as model for situation of electrons in a metal, and plot of energy versus wave number from Eq. (2.6).

quantum mechanics, *the particle in a box.* In the one-dimensional case the Schrödinger equation (2) is

$$\frac{d^2\psi}{dx^2} + \frac{8\pi^2 m}{h^2}(E - V)\psi = 0 \tag{2.4}$$

Here E is the total energy and V is the potential energy of the particle of mass m, and $\psi(x)$ is the *wave function* associated with the particle. What shall take the boundary conditions to be, at $x = 0$ and a, $V = \infty$. Actually, as shown in Fig. 2.3, $V = \phi$, but $V = \infty$ is a satisfactory approximation for electrons in low-energy levels. The solutions of Eq. (2.4) are the standing waves[1]

$$\psi = e^{ikx} = e^{i\pi n x/a} \tag{2.5}$$

where **k** is called the *wave number.* It is related to the momentum p of the electron considered as a particle by $\mathbf{k} = 2\pi p/h$, and to the wavelength λ of the electron considered as a wave by $\mathbf{k} = 2\pi/\lambda$. The energy levels are given by

$$E_n = \frac{\mathbf{k}^2 h^2}{8\pi^2 m} = \frac{n^2 h^2}{8ma^2} \tag{2.6}$$

---

[1] The complex exponential notation for periodic functions is convenient for adding waves, taking derivatives of wave functions, and so on. It is equivalent to a linear combination of a sine and cosine function, since $e^{i\theta} = \cos\theta + i\sin\theta$. See Courant and Robbins (3).

These energy levels are in principle discrete but they are so closely packed together that they form an effectively continuous band. If we plot the energy E versus the wave number $\mathbf{k}$ we obtain a parabola as shown in Fig. 2.3.

When we begin to assign electrons to the energy levels of Eq. (2.6), however, we must require that the allowed wave functions follow the Pauli principle. We can put just two electrons of opposite spin into each level of quantum number n. When this is done, that level is filled. We must proceed to the next higher level for the next pair of electrons. The result is obvious—all the lowest levels are filled with pairs of electrons until they reach some maximum value of energy E_F. If we draw the *distribution function*, the probability of filling a level $P(E)$, as a function of E, we find the result shown in Fig. 2.4: $P(E) = 1$ until we reach the maximum level E_F after which it falls to $P(E) = 0$.

This distribution function is called the *Fermi–Dirac distribution function*. It is the one to be expected when elementary particles are distributed in translational energy levels with the requirement that they follow the Pauli exclusion principle—no more than two particles of opposite spin being allowed in a given level. At any temperature above absolute zero, some electrons at

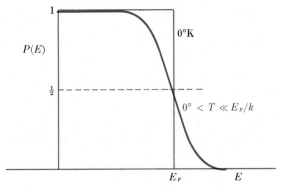

Fig. 2.4. The Fermi–Dirac distribution function for energies of electrons in a metal.

the top of the distribution may occupy levels higher than E_F. The distribution thus modified is shown as a colored line in Fig. 2.4.

The mathematical expression for the distribution function as a function of temperature and energy is

$$P(E) = \frac{1}{e^{(E-E_F)/kT} + 1} \tag{2.7}$$

Note that when $P(E) = \frac{1}{2}$ (a fifty-fifty probability of finding the level occupied) then $E = E_F$. This value E_F is called the *Fermi energy*. It plays an important part in the theory of metals and semiconductors. In metals the Fermi energy acts as an effective cutoff level for the allowed energies of the electrons. We can imagine the electrons to form a sort of sea having a depth equal to the Fermi energy. At ordinary temperatures only a small fraction of the total number of electrons will ever have an energy much above the Fermi sea level.

It can be shown that the Fermi energy is the electrochemical potential of the electron (4). If two phases α and β are in equilibrium, the electrochemical potential $\bar{\mu}_j^{\alpha}$ of any component j that occurs in phase α must equal the electrochemical potential of that component in phase β if it occurs there:

$$\bar{\mu}_j^{\alpha} = \bar{\mu}_j^{\beta}$$

The Fermi energy is thus important in defining the condition for equilibrium of electrons between phases. The electrochemical potential $\bar{\mu}$ is the same as the partial molar Gibbs function G of chemical thermodynamics (5).

As long as $E_F \gg kT$, the $P(E)$ function has the general shape shown in Fig. 2.4, but as temperature increases it gradually spreads out and finally at very high temperatures it would begin to look like an ordinary Maxwell–Boltzmann distribution function for gas molecules. Thus when $E_F \gg kT$ the electron distribution function behaves like a quantum-mechanical one. In this case the electron gas is said to be *degenerate*. At an ordinary temperature, say 1000°K, $kT = 0.086$ eV, whereas for gold $E_F = 5.51$ eV, for sodium $E_F = 3.12$ eV, which are typical values for metals. Thus, the electron gas in a metal is usually degenerate and cannot be treated as an ordinary Maxwellian gas. We recall that the Maxwell distribution function is the basis for the equipartition principle, the translational energy averaged over the Maxwell distribution being $\frac{3}{2}kT$.

We can see now why the electron gas does not contribute to the heat capacity of metals. As a metal is heated the only way an electron can take up energy would be to move into a somewhat higher allowed energy level. But a typical electron is buried deep in the Fermi sea, and there are no empty levels into which it can move, since each level above the electron is already occupied by a pair of electrons with opposing spins. Only the relatively few electrons at the top of the distribution function can find empty levels into which to move. These form the so-called *Maxwellian tail* of the Fermi distribution. They are the only electrons that contribute to the heat capacity. Thus, at ordinary temperatures the electronic heat capacity is almost negligible.

You may be surprised that all the electrons can contribute to the conductivity, since in order to do this they must take energy from the electric field and move into higher levels. What happens in this case, however, is a shift of the entire set of electron-energy levels from lower to higher values. The Fermi distribution is shifted bodily by the applied field. Thus the electrons can acquire an average drift velocity in the field without violating the Pauli exclusion principle.

2.5 DENSITY OF STATES

The Fermi–Dirac distribution function $P(E)$ of Eq. (2.7) gives the probability that a state of energy E is occupied by an electron. The number of energy states available in any particular range of energy is given by the *density-of-states* function $N(E)$. Then the number of electrons $n(E)$ actually in a range of energy from E to $E + dE$ will be given by the product of $P(E)$ and $N(E)$,

$$n(E)\ dE = P(E)N(E)\ dE \qquad (2.8)$$

We can readily derive $N(E)$ for the case of free electrons. By extension of Eq. (2.6), electrons in a cubic box of side a have allowed energy levels specified by three quantum numbers n_1, n_2, n_3.

$$E = \frac{h^2}{8ma^2} (n_1^2 + n_2^2 + n_3^2) \qquad (2.9)$$

Hence,

$$\frac{8mEa^2}{h^2} = n_1^2 + n_2^2 + n_3^2 \qquad (2.10)$$

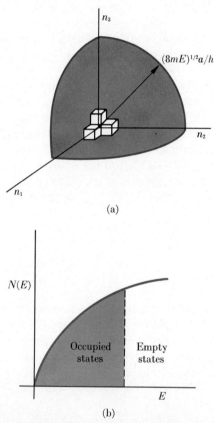

(a)

(b)

Fig. 2.5 (a) The number of states corresponding to sets of quantum numbers n_1, n_2, n_3 with energy less than E is volume of positive octant of sphere. (b) Plot of density of states function of Eq. (2.11).

If we plot n_1, n_2, and n_3 along three Cartesian coordinate axes, any point corresponding to a set of three integral values of n_1, n_2, n_3 will correspond to an allowed energy state for the electron. We can think of this three-dimensional space (n space) as being divided into cells of unit volume, with one such cell for every set of three quantum numbers n_1, n_2, n_3. This representation is depicted in Fig. 2.5a. Now we note that Eq. (2.10) is the equation of a sphere of radius $(8mEa^2/h^2)^{1/2}$ in n space, the volume of which would be $\frac{4}{3}\pi(8mEa^2/h^2)^{3/2}$. Since the quantum numbers can have only positive values, the number of cells (sets of quantum numbers) corresponding to states with energies less than E will be the volume of the positive octant of this sphere. Hence, the number per unit volume is

$$2 \cdot \frac{1}{8} \cdot \frac{4}{3}\pi \left(\frac{8mE}{h^2}\right)^{3/2}$$

The factor of two arises from the fact that each state can hold two electrons of opposite spin. By differentiating this expression we obtain the density-of-states function for free electrons,

$$N(E)\,dE = \frac{\pi}{2}\left(\frac{8m}{h^2}\right)^{3/2} E^{1/2}\,dE \tag{2.11}$$

The shape of this $N(E)$ function is depicted in Fig. 2.5b. We shall see later how it can be determined experimentally.

2.6 EFFECT OF ATOMIC CORES

Although we can learn quite a lot about electrons in metals from the free electron Fermi–Dirac gas model, we obviously cannot learn the reason for the most remarkable fact of all: that electrons move freely through metals despite the fact that these are closely packed structures. To understand how this happens and to see how a metal is bonded together we must turn our attention to a more realistic model, one that includes effects due to atomic cores.

If the atoms of gold were far enough apart, each atom would hold its own electrons and we should have simply an array of isolated gold atoms, ordered if we like, but not resembling a metal in closest packing. This extreme case is quite useful, nevertheless, for describing the inner electrons. It is called the *tight-binding approximation* to indicate that the electrons are tightly bound to the atomic nuclei. (The name is certainly *not* meant to imply that the metal atoms are tightly bound together, since they are only loosely coupled when this approximation is valid.)

If we now move the atoms together, reducing the internuclear distance R, so that outer electron orbitals[2] overlap, we can no longer describe the system simply in terms of atomic orbitals of isolated atoms. You are probably already familiar with an important example of what happens when atomic orbitals overlap, namely, the basic case of two hydrogen atoms brought together to form a hydrogen molecule. You can think of bringing together a whole collection of gold atoms in an ordered array as a grandiose extension of what happens when you bring together two hydrogen atoms.

As two hydrogen atoms overlap each other we can no longer say that electron 1 belongs unequivocally to proton A and electron 2 to proton B. In terms of atomic orbitals $1s_A$ and $1s_B$, a new molecular orbital is formed, which is a linear combination of atomic orbitals. We write it mathematically as

$$\psi_{mo} = (1s_A + \lambda 1s_B) \tag{2.12}$$

Since A and B are identical the only reasonable values of λ are ± 1. We thus get two new molecular orbitals from our two original $1s$ atomic orbitals:

$$\psi_1 = (1s_A + 1s_B) \qquad \psi_2 = (1s_A - 1s_B) \tag{2.13}$$

From the elementary theory of chemical bonding you may remember that ψ_1 is called a *bonding orbital* since it leads to concentration of electronic charge near the nuclei, and ψ_2 is called an *antibonding orbital* since it leads to depletion of electronic charge near the nuclei (6).

Each original $1s$ orbital could hold two electrons with opposite spins in accord with the Pauli principle. Since the two $1s$ orbitals gave rise to two molecular orbitals it follows that each of the mo-

---

[2] An *orbital* is a wave function ψ which is a function of the spacial coordinates of one electron, for example, $\psi(x_1, y_1, z_1)$.

lecular orbitals that are formed can also hold a pair of electrons of opposite spins. If we brought three hydrogen atoms together we would get three molecular orbitals, and in general if we brought N atoms together we would get a spray of N molecular orbitals. We might expect that half of these would be at higher energies than the originals and that half would be lower. You can probably see already what we are leading up to. If the atoms that make a metal are gradually brought together by reducing the internuclear distance R, we obtain closely packed sprays of orbitals as shown in Fig. 2.6. When many atoms are involved, the energies of the individual metallic orbitals are so crowded together that they form an effectively continuous band of allowed energy levels.

2.7 A ONE-DIMENSIONAL MODEL FOR A METAL

It is worthwhile trying to get a more quantitative understanding of what happens to electrons in a metal under the influence of the regular array of atomic cores. We turn to a one-dimensional model since the mathematics is thereby greatly simplified. We shall use a model originally given by Kronig and Penney. These authors asked the question: What do the wave functions and energy levels look like for motion of electrons in a periodic one-dimensional potential? They chose a row of square potential wells as shown in Fig. 2.7a and proceeded to solve the Schrödinger equation for the motion of a single electron in this potential. This is really quite a simple problem for students of quantum mechanics.

According to a basic theorem of differential equations (7), if $\psi_0(x)$ is a solution of the Schrödinger equation in free space, a solution in a potential that is periodic with period a, that is, $V(x) = V(x + a)$, is a product of $\psi_0(x)$ and another function $u(x)$ which is itself periodic with period a. Thus the wave function of the electron in the periodic potential has the form

$$\psi(x) = \psi_0(x)u(x) \qquad (2.14)$$

Functions of this form are called *Bloch functions*. We already know the solution $\psi_0(x)$ for the electron in one-dimensional field-free space. It is a running wave which can be written as a sine or

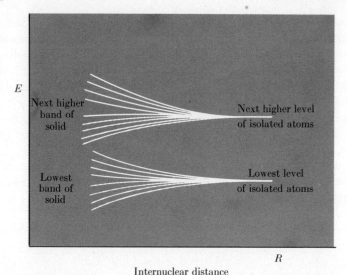

E

Next higher band of solid

Next higher level of isolated atoms

Lowest band of solid

Lowest level of isolated atoms

R

Internuclear distance

Fig. 2.6. Overlap of electron distributions of atoms causes sharp energy levels of isolated atoms to broaden into bands in the solid.

cosine function or more generally in the form e^{ikx}, where **k** is equal to $2\pi/\lambda$, λ being the wavelength of the electron. This running wave thus represents the behavior of the free electron. In the presence of the periodic potential, the running wave is modulated to give

$$\psi(x) = e^{ikx} u(x) \qquad (2.15)$$

This result may not seem like very much but it is in fact extremely important. It shows that the wave function for the electron itself has the periodicity of the crystal lattice. Consequently, just as we saw previously for x rays scattered from crystal structures, or for vibrations of atoms in such structures, only certain wavelengths (that is, energies) are permissible for electrons in crystals. The motion of an electron in a periodic potential function is such that its energy is restricted to certain allowed levels which are crowded together so as to give allowed bands of energy levels.

These allowed bands are separated by gaps in energy. Energy levels that lie in the gaps are not allowed: they represent energy states which are absolutely prohibited for electrons in a periodic potential.

An interesting way to show this result is to plot the energy of an electron E versus its wave number $\mathbf{k}$. For the free electron

$$E = \frac{p^2}{2m} = \frac{h^2\mathbf{k}^2}{8\pi^2 m} \qquad \text{since } p = \frac{h\mathbf{k}}{2\pi} \qquad (2.16)$$

This is the equation of a parabola as was shown in Fig. 2.3. The effect of the periodic potential is to introduce energy gaps at certain values of $\mathbf{k}$ as shown in Fig. 2.7b. In the one-dimensional case we have outlined, these energy gaps occur at $\mathbf{k} = \pm\pi/a$, $\pm2\pi/a$, $\ldots$, $\pm n\pi/a$. This result is shown in the figure. For the lowest values of $\mathbf{k}$, the E versus $\mathbf{k}$ curve coincides with the parabola characteristic of free electrons. As $\mathbf{k}$ approaches $\pm\pi/a$, however, the rise in energy flattens and at $\mathbf{k} = \pm\pi/a$ there is an abrupt discontinuity in E, over a range of E values which are completely forbidden energy states for the electron. The pattern of energy levels is thus a band of allowed levels, followed by an energy gap, then a second band of allowed levels, and so on.

When you recall that the wave number or momentum of an electron determines its wavelength, the condition for a discontinuity $\mathbf{k} = n\pi/a$ appears to have the same mathematical form as the Bragg relation $n\lambda = 2a \sin\theta$. In a one-dimensional case, $\theta = 90°$ and $\mathbf{k} = n\pi/a$ as we have seen.

If an electron (wave) is incident on a periodic line of atoms at exactly the wavelength specified by the Bragg condition, it is not transmitted but is totally "reflected." Thus, we have a physically clear picture of why electrons with certain momenta cannot pass through a crystal structure. These momenta specify wavelengths for which Bragg "reflections" must occur. In three dimensions, of course, the value of the forbidden wavelength must depend on the direction of incidence. We shall return to that case shortly.

There is nothing mysterious about a gap of forbidden energies for an electron. We find such a situation in the simple case of the hydrogen atom. There we describe separate levels corresponding to energy values (eigenvalues) for which solutions ψ of the wave

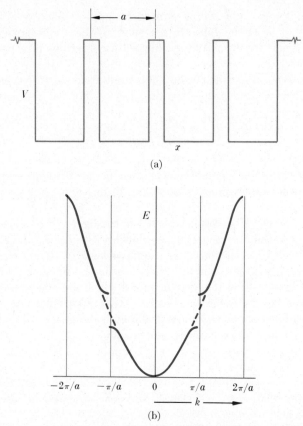

Fig. 2.7. (a) **One-dimensional model for periodic potential acting on electron in a metal. (b) Energy versus wave number for motion of an electron in the one-dimensional periodic potential of Fig. 2.7a. The range of allowed k values from $-\pi/a$ to $+\pi/a$ is the first Brillouin zone for this system.**

equation can be found.   In the case of a periodic array of atoms we have bands of tightly spaced energy levels separated by gaps of forbidden energy.   We have already seen how such a result might be expected as an array of hydrogen atoms are brought together along a line.   It seems physically clear that the existence of energy bands is due to the fact that each electron can occupy many different positions. If there was a moderate departure from periodicity of structure, we should still expect to get energy bands and gaps. For example, molten gold is still a metal and quite a good conductor of electricity. The periodic potential is a sufficient but not a necessary condition for a band structure. Its great virtue is that it can be treated theoretically by elegant mathematical methods and thus opens the way to a rigorous theory of the solid state. The problem solved by Kronig and Penney involved only a single electron and hence avoided the serious difficulties caused by interactions between electrons. Just as in the case of the quantum theory of atomic and molecular structure the major difficulties in the quantum theory of solids come from the complexities of the many-body problem of several interacting electrons.

2.8 BRILLOUIN ZONES

The zones in **k** space which correspond to allowed energies for motion of an electron in a solid are called *Brillouin zones*. The first two zones in the one-dimensional case are seen in Fig. 2.7b. The first zone extends between $\mathbf{k} = -\pi/a$ and $\mathbf{k} = \pi/a$. The second zone is the range of **k** from $-2\pi/a$ to $-\pi/a$ plus the range from π/a to $2\pi/a$.

When we turn to a real three-dimensional crystal we find that the zone structure still exists but it is different for different directions in the **k** space of the crystal. Just as the coordinates x, y, z specify the location of a point in position space, so the coordinates $\mathbf{k}_x$, $\mathbf{k}_y$, and $\mathbf{k}_z$ specify a point in **k** space, that is, a certain value of the vector from the origin which specifies the momentum of the electron.

Recalling the relation between wavelength λ and momentum mv as given by the de Broglie equation,

$$\lambda = \frac{h}{mv} \tag{2.17}$$

the wave number $\mathbf{k} = 2\pi/\lambda$, and hence $\mathbf{k} = 2\pi mv/h$. We see therefore that wave number and momentum are strictly proportional.

Consider a beam of electrons incident on a set of crystal planes with spacing d. You can think of this beam as an electron wave with wave number given by the vector $\mathbf{k}$ at angle θ to the surface. The normal component of $\mathbf{k}$ is

$$\mathbf{k}_n = \mathbf{k} \sin \theta \qquad (2.18)$$

Now since $n\lambda = 2d \sin \theta$, $2\pi n/\mathbf{k} = 2d \sin \theta$, or $\pi n/d = \mathbf{k}_n$. Thus we find that

$$\mathbf{k}_n = \frac{\pi n}{d} \qquad (2.19)$$

These are the values of $\mathbf{k}_n$ for which the electron cannot pass through the crystal structure. They are therefore the values corresponding to discontinuities in the allowed energy levels, that is, to the zone boundaries. The usual way to show these is to draw them in $\mathbf{k}$ space, by plotting the surface of discontinuity in a space in which the distance from the origin is proportional to the value of $\mathbf{k}$. Equation (2.19) shows that Bragg reflecting planes with largest spacings have smallest values of $\mathbf{k}_n$.

Let us first consider these planes in a simple cubic lattice. The planes with the largest spacing ($d = a$) are the {100} planes. The direction cosines of the normals to these planes would be (± 1, 0, 0) (0, ± 1, 0) (0, 0, ± 1). Thus the first zone in $\mathbf{k}$ space is bounded by the planes

$$\mathbf{k}_x = \frac{\pm \pi}{a} \qquad \mathbf{k}_y = \frac{\pm \pi}{a} \qquad \mathbf{k}_z = \frac{\pm \pi}{a}$$

The first zone is therefore a cube with faces π/a from the origin, as shown in Fig. 2.8.

The next set of reflecting planes are the {110} with spacing $a_0/2^{1/2}$. Corresponding planes in $\mathbf{k}$ space would be

$$\pm \mathbf{k}_x \pm \mathbf{k}_y = \frac{2\pi}{a}$$

$$\pm \mathbf{k}_x \pm \mathbf{k}_z = \frac{2\pi}{a}$$

$$\pm \mathbf{k}_y \pm \mathbf{k}_z = \frac{2\pi}{a}$$

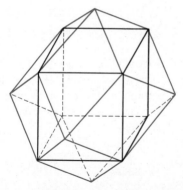

Fig. 2.8.   First two Brillouin zones for simple cubic lattice. The first zone is the cube of volume $8\pi^3/a^3$ in k space.   The second zone is the k space between the cube and the circumscribed dodecahedron.

These twelve planes outline the dodecahedron shown in Fig. 2.8. The second Brillouin zone is the space between the faces of the cube bounding zone (1) and the faces of the dodecahedron bounding zone (2).

A case of more direct interest to us in connection with the gold structure is the first Brillouin zone for the face-centered cubic lattice. The situation here is somewhat different. The {100} planes do not exhibit Bragg reflection since they are interleaved by an equivalent set of planes passing through the face-centered positions. The same is true of the {110} planes. We find the largest spacing that satisfies the Bragg condition, therefore, with the {111} planes at a spacing of $a_0/3^{1/2}$. In the k-space figure bounded by the planes parallel to these, however, we find that in some directions, for example, toward the vertices of the resulting octahedra, there would be another set of planes which would be reached first, namely, those derived from the {200} planes of the face-centered cubic lattice. Thus the zone boundaries arise partly from planes derived from {111} and partly from planes derived from {200}. The resultant Brillouin zone has the form shown in Fig. 2.9.

2.9   THE SURFACE OF THE FERMI SEA

In the one-dimensional cases (Figs. 2.3 and 2.7b), we plotted the energies of the electrons against **k**. In the three-dimensional case we show the same thing in different ways. In the case of a free electron we can easily visualize these surfaces in **k** space. The energy levels were given by

$$E_n = \frac{h^2}{8ma^2}\,(\mathbf{k}_x^2 + \mathbf{k}_y^2 + \mathbf{k}_z^2) \qquad (2.20)$$

This is the equation of a sphere of radius $(\mathbf{k}_x^2 + \mathbf{k}_y^2 + \mathbf{k}_z^2)^{1/2}$. Thus the surfaces of constant energy for free electrons are spheres in **k** space. We can draw the contours of the energy surface by connecting points of equal energy in **k** space. In this way we get a nice picture of how the electrons can fill up energy levels within a Brillouin zone. Two such contours are shown in Fig. 2.9. Near

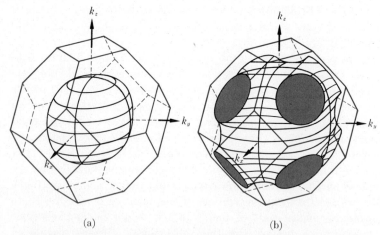

(a)   (b)

Fig. 2.9.   The first Brillouin zone of face-centered cubic structure with surfaces of constant energy of electrons shown for (a) nearly free electrons near bottom of zone and (b) electrons at zone boundary. [After N. F. Mott and H. Jones (8).]

the center of the zone the electrons are virtually free and behave like an electron gas. The energy is then given by equation (2.20). Thus at energies well below the zone boundaries, the surfaces of constant energy are represented as spheres within the Brillouin zone (Fig. 2.9a). As more electrons are added, however, the energy surfaces approach the boundaries of the zone. Since they cannot transgress these boundaries, the spherical surface becomes distorted by bulging out toward the zonal plane. Thus, we have near the top of the zone an energy surface like that shown in Fig. 2.9b. The electrons near the zone boundary no longer behave like a free electron gas.

An important result now appears. We have two possible cases. (1) Points in the second zone may all have higher energies than those in the first zone. There will then be a gap of unallowed energies no matter what direction we take. (2) Some points in the second zone have lower energies than some in the first zone. In this case, there will be an overlap between the two zones so that for certain changes in momentum an electron can pass from one zone to the next without jumping an energy gap. As the electrons are added gradually and fill up the allowed energy levels, they will never meet an actual gap of forbidden energies.

On the basis of this model we can make a good distinction between metals and insulators. We shall always be able to get the electrical conductivity characteristic of a metal provided the electrons do not completely fill the first zone or, if they do, provided that the second zone overlaps the first *in some directions*. On the other hand, we shall have an insulator in case the available number of electrons completely fills the first zone and there is *always* a considerable gap in energy before the empty second zone can be reached.

The occurrence of zone boundaries has an important effect on the density of allowed states for electrons, the $N(E)$ function of Eq. (2.11). You will remember that electrons cannot swim in the depths of the Fermi sea—only on the surface are they mobile. The motion of an electron can be represented by a rolling over the Fermi surface. We see a good example of this in the contours shown in Fig. 2.9. In the case of a half-filled zone, the electrons at the surface can move freely in any direction. When the Fermi sea touches the zone boundary, however, the electron cannot have a velocity normal to that boundary. Thus if we plot the number of allowed states as a function of E, we find that the curve starts out like the free electron curve of Fig. 2.5b but there are sharp breaks at those values of E corresponding to the zone boundaries. In the case of a face-centered cubic metal like gold, there will be two such breaks. One occurs when the zone boundary derived from $\{111\}$ planes is reached, and the other when the boundary derived from $\{200\}$ planes is reached. We thus get a plot of $N(E)$, the number density of allowed states of energy E, versus E such as that shown in Fig. 2.10. In the case of pure gold, each atom contributes one valence electron, so that the zone is only about half filled. We show the occupied energy states by the shaded region on the energy plot in the figure. Thus gold is a good conductor because there are always plenty of empty allowed states in **k** space above the topmost filled state.

2.10   EXPERIMENTAL MAPPING OF THE FERMI SEA

There are several interesting ways to study experimentally the properties of the Fermi sea of electrons.

If we simply wish to know the width of the allowed energy band with some indication of the density of its population by electrons, we can employ soft x-ray emission spectra. X rays with wavelengths in about the region from 20 Å to 100 Å are called "soft" because of their low penetrating power in solids. High-speed electrons incident on a crystal target drive other electrons out of lower levels, such as K and L shells. When an electron from the occupied upper band drops into the resulting hole, a quantum of x radiation is emitted. In a gaseous atom the energy levels are all quite sharp and the emission spectra consist of sharp lines. In the case of an atom in a solid, the inner electronic energy levels ($1s$, $2s$, $2p$, etc.) are still sharp but the outermost levels have broadened to bands of energy. Thus, the x-ray spectra that originate from electronic transitions between the levels in the broad outer band and those in the inner K and L shells cover a range of energy that corresponds to the range of the energy band. In fact, the

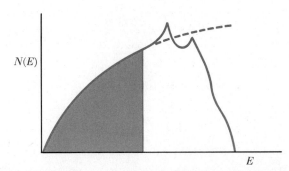

Fig. 2.10. Density of states function for face-centered cubic structure of gold. The shaded area shows occupied states in gold. The dashed curve is the free-electron function [Eq. (2.11)].

intensity soft x-ray emission plotted against energy E looks exactly like the $N(E)$ versus E plot exemplified in Fig. 2.10. The energy (wavelength) distribution of these x rays depends on the width of the band from which they came. Such soft x-ray emission spectra thus give valuable information about band structures of solids, not only metals, but insulators and semiconductors as well.

The Fermi surface shown in Fig. 2.9 can extend throughout many unit cells if the necks in the [111] directions are joined together with similar surfaces in adjacent cells. We thus get a picture of the continuous zone structure, a section of which is shown in Fig. 2.11. Electron orbits can be represented as paths over the zonal surface shown. A great variety of paths are possible, some of which have been given picturesque names: rosette, dogsbone, neck, belly, monster.

In the presence of a magnetic field these paths may be closed, and they can be studied by the phenomenon of *cyclotron resonance*. The motion of the electron over the closed orbit has a certain characteristic frequency. When the metal is placed in an alternating electromagnetic field which sweeps through a range of frequencies, energy will be absorbed from the field when its frequency matches the cyclotron resonance frequency of the electronic orbit. A de-

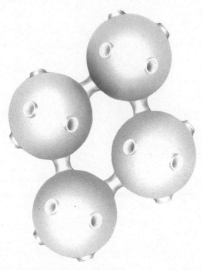

Fig. 2.11. Continuous Fermi surface extending through adjacent unit cells in gold structure. See the dogsbone.

tailed picture of the Fermi surface can be drawn so as to accord with the data obtained in this way.

A more indirect method is based on the periodic variations of magnetic susceptibility with magnetic field strength. This phenomenon, called the *de Haas–van Alphen effect* is due to the influence of magnetic field on the occupation of various parts of the Fermi surface. It must be measured at very low temperatures. Since it depends also on the exact direction of the external field, it can often lead to a detailed map of the Fermi surface. We may expect that in the future these mappings of the Fermi sea will provide a basis for a much deeper understanding of the chemical and catalytic properties of metals.

2.11   ALLOYS

On a structural basis we can distinguish two kinds of solid solution. In an *interstitial* solid solution, the solid atoms occupy interstitial sites in the host structure. We shall discuss examples of these in a later chapter. They are not of particular interest in the study of intermetallic solutions, which almost all belong to the second type, the *substitutional* solid solution. In a substitutional solid solution dissolved atoms replace atoms in the host structure.

In some cases complete intersolubility is possible. Thus silver and gold are mutually soluble in all proportions. In other cases a distinct solubility limit appears, when the so-called alpha substitutional solid solution no longer occurs and some new phase intervenes. An example of this is the gold-cadmium system in which the face-centered cubic (fcc) α solution becomes unstable at about 65 atom % Au and a body-centered cubic (bcc) structure is formed. (The exact transition composition depends on the temperature.)

Hume-Rothery was the first to point out the importance of electron concentration in determining the composition limits of alloy phases. To see how his model works in a given case, consider the alloys of cadmium with gold. Cadmium contributes two electrons and gold one electron. As we replace Au atoms with Cd to form the α substitutional solid solution, we add an extra electron to the system for each Au replaced by Cd. The lowest zone in the fcc structure can hold just two electrons per atom, but when the electron per atom ratio reaches 1.362, the surface of the Fermi sea is lapping at the zone boundary. The corresponding atom per cent gold would be

$$1.00 \ X_{Au} + 2.00 \ (1 - X_{Au}) = 1.362$$
$$X_{Au} = 0.638$$

The experimental value for the limit of solubility of Cd in Au is $X_{Au} = 0.65$. Many illustrative examples of this kind could be cited from other alloy systems, so that the Hume-Rothery rules have considerable validity.

Electron concentrations and Brillouin zone boundaries, however, are not the only factors important in alloy structures. Sizes of atoms, relative electronegativities, and London forces between core electrons are also important. The factors involved are so complex that at present most of the questions as to why certain alloy compositions and structures exist cannot be solved by pure

theory. Nevertheless, it is fair to say that when we consider the
stable range of an alloy structure, the first thing to do is to account
for the electrons.

2.12   ELECTRON CATALYSIS

We can extend the conclusion in the last section to state that
whenever we are dealing with any chemical or physical properties
of an alloy we should look at the electron concentration in the occupied zones. Effects that otherwise would appear mysterious
then often become quite understandable. A striking example is the
work of Couper and Eley on catalytic properties of gold-palladium
alloys. They studied the para-ortho hydrogen conversion on the
surface of alloy wires. The reaction is believed to proceed through
a triatomic activated complex in the absorbed layer:

$$\text{H--H--H}$$
$$\text{M--H} + p\text{-H}_2 \rightarrow \qquad \text{M} \qquad \rightarrow o\text{-H}_2 + \text{M--H}$$

where M stands for the metal surface.

The activation energy E_a for the reaction was measured at
different alloy compositions. The E_a for pure gold is 17.5 kcal
mole^{-1}. This is decreased to 8.5 kcal mole^{-1} by addition of few
per cent palladium. The E_a remains effectively constant at this
figure until about 37% Pd when it drops sharply to 3.5 kcal mole^{-1},
the same value as for pure Pd.

Each atom of Pd contributes an extra electron which goes into
the d band. As long as the d band is not filled completely it can ac-
cept electrons from the adsorbed hydrogen and hence take part
in the surface metal-to-hydrogen bond that facilitates the catalytic
exchange reaction. When the d band is filled, it is presumably
necessary to excite some electrons into the $4s$ band in order to make
the M--H bond, and hence the activation energy is much higher.

2.13   ORDER-DISORDER TRANSITIONS

If a 50 atom % alloy of gold and copper is annealed for a
long time at temperatures below 394°C, additional lines can be

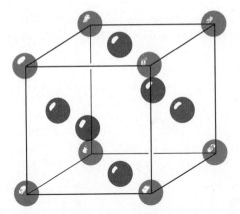

Fig. 2.12.   **Ordered superstructure in Au–Cu alloy**

found in its x-ray diffraction diagram besides those characteristic of the fcc structure.   These are called *superstructure lines* and are explained by a transition from random solid solution to an ordered structure.   The nature of this ordered structure is shown in Fig. 2.12.   All the corner positions of the unit cells are occupied by Au atoms and all the face-centered positions by Cu atoms.[3]   If this ordered structure is heated above 394°C, it reverts to the random structure, making a typical order-disorder transition.   Note that the random structure, having the higher entropy, must be the more stable form at higher temperature.   Many properties of alloys, such as electrical conductivity and heat capacity, display marked variations at such transitions.

Alloy superstructures are of great interest as prototypes of the ordering found in ferromagnetic and ferroelectric crystals, which we shall mention later (Chapter 4).   The theory of phase transitions is one of the most active branches of statistical mechanics applied to the solid state.   It is believed that if we can understand completely a simple order-disorder transition, we shall then be able to use the same kind of theory to understand the more difficult problem of the transition from solid to liquid state.   We should like

[3] Reversal of these assignments of course gives identical structure.

to be able to predict the melting points of Au, NaCl, and all other crystals from pure theory. As of today we are a long way from this goal.

2.14 POINT DEFECTS IN METALS

One of the earliest quantitative studies of diffusion in the solid state was made in 1892 by the English metallurgist, Roberts-Austen. His data for the diffusion coefficient D of gold in lead as a function of the absolute temperature T follow an Arrhenius-type equation

$$D = D_0 \exp\left(\frac{-E_a}{RT}\right) \qquad (2.21)$$

where E_a is the activation energy for diffusion. In this case

$$D_{Au}(Pb) = 0.49 \exp\left(\frac{-13 \text{ kcal}}{RT}\right) \text{ cm}^2 \text{ sec}^{-1}$$

so that $E_a = 13$ kcal mole^{-1}.

From the empirical equation we can compute that at 300°C $D = 0.54 \times 10^{-5}$ cm^2 sec^{-1}. The value for diffusion of NaCl in water at 25°C is 1.61×10^{-5} cm^2 sec^{-1}. It seems rather amazing that diffusion in a solid metal can be of the same order of magnitude as diffusion of salt in aqueous solution. Such results at first seemed quite impossible to explain. Only after the work in the 1930's of Frenkel and Schottky on point defects did the situation become clear—metal structures must contain vacancies which provide relatively easy mechanisms for diffusion to occur. We have already discussed the occurrence of such vacancies in the NaCl structure. We now see that vacancies (and other point defects) also occur in metal structures.

In pure gold, the self-diffusion coefficient (measured with radioactive gold tracer atoms) is given by

$$D = 0.16 \exp\left(\frac{-53.0 \text{ kcal}}{RT}\right) \text{ cm}^2 \text{ sec}^{-1} \qquad (2.22)$$

The activation energy of 53.0 kcal is much higher than that for diffusion of gold in lead. The cohesive energy of gold is also much higher than that of lead, as witnessed by its melting point of 1336°K compared to 600°K for the latter. Thus, to create or move vacancies requires much more energy in gold than in lead. At 1326°K, just 10° below its melting point, the self-diffusion coefficient of gold from Eq. (2.22) would be

$$D = 0.16 \exp\left(\frac{-53000}{1.986 \times 1326}\right) = 0.16 \, e^{-20.1}$$
$$= 0.16 \times 10^{-20.1/2.303} = 3.1 \times 10^{-10} \text{ cm}^2 \text{ sec}^{-1}$$

With D of this magnitude, an atom of gold would require on the average about six months to migrate 1 mm in the solid (at just below its melting point).

If a metal is placed under stress, the migration of atoms, through vacancies in the structure, can be greatly increased. A slow flow of the metal can occur, which is known as *vacancy creep.* Such creep becomes large as the grain size of the metal is reduced (that is, the size of the individual crystallites that comprise the metal specimen). The boundaries between grains act as sources and sinks of vacancies. In the metal under stress, atoms move (via vacancies) from surfaces under compression to those under tension, so that the metal actually slowly flows to relieve the applied stress. You can imagine the catastrophic results that such creep might cause if the metal in question was a cable supporting a chair lift on a ski slope or a rotor in a high-speed centrifuge. Engineers who design metal parts subject to stress never forget to calculate the maximum rate of creep possible under working conditions. The problem obviously can become rather frightful when the part is subject to a combination of high temperature and high stress.

REFERENCES

(1) R. M. Hochstrasser, *Behavior of Electrons in Atoms* (New York: Benjamin, 1964), Chapter IV—The Pauli Principle and the Electronic Structure of Atoms.

(2) W. Heitler, *Elementary Wave Mechanics* (Oxford: Clarendon Press, 1956), Chapter II—Derivation of the Wave Equation.

(3) R. Courant and W. Robbins, *What is Mathematics?* (New York and London: Oxford University Press, 1941), p. 88–100.

(4) N. B. Hannay, *Semiconductors* (New York: Reinhold, 1959), p. 24–27.

(5) J. G. Kirkwood and L. Oppenheim, *Chemical Thermodynamics* (New York: McGraw-Hill, 1961), Chapter 13—Thermodynamic Theory of Electrochemical Systems.

(6) H. B. Gray, *Electrons and Chemical Bonding* (New York: Benjamin, 1964), Chapter II—Diatomic Molecules.

(7) E. T. Whittaker and G. N. Watson, *Modern Analysis* (Cambridge: Cambridge University Press, 1952), p. 412 (Floquet's Theorem).

(8) N. F. Mott and H. Jones, *Properties of Metals and Alloys* (New York and London: Oxford University Press, 1936).

III

Silicon

B ETWEEN 1940 AND 1950 a revolution in the science of electronics led to the replacement of large hot vacuum tubes by
tiny cold transistors. The transistor and similar devices were designed on the basis of a good understanding of the theory of semiconductors, a class of materials neither metals nor insulators, and
thus adapted in some respects to act as both at the same time.
Silicon and germanium have been the most important semiconducting crystals in applications of solid state electronics.

3.1 STRUCTURE OF SILICON

Silicon and germanium crystallize in a cubic structure identical with that of diamond; grey tin also has this structure. It is
shown in Fig. 3.1. You will notice at once that it is not a close-

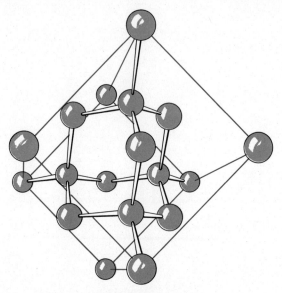

Fig. 3.1. Cubic unit cell of the silicon structure (drawn by F. M. Thayer). [After G. H. Wannier (1).]

packed structure. Each atom of silicon has only four neighbors, arrayed at the vertices of a regular tetrahedron. This geometry reminds us of the tetrahedral covalent bonding of four groups to a carbon or silicon atom in its most usual valence state, as in methane or silicon tetrafluoride.

The cubic unit cell contains eight atoms, four at the corners and face-centered positions, and four occupying half of the eight possible tetrahedral positions in the unit cell. We can thus base the structure on a fcc lattice, with two atoms associated with each lattice point. The positions of the atoms can be designated as [corners (000), faces $(\frac{1}{2}\frac{1}{2}0,\ 0\frac{1}{2}\frac{1}{2},\ \frac{1}{2}0\frac{1}{2})$, tetrahedral sites $(\frac{1}{4}\frac{1}{4}\frac{1}{4},\ \frac{3}{4}\frac{1}{4}\frac{3}{4},\ \frac{1}{4}\frac{3}{4}\frac{3}{4},\ \frac{3}{4}\frac{3}{4}\frac{1}{4})]$.

Detailed x-ray work on diamond has given direct experimental data on the location of electrons in the structure. X rays are scattered by the distribution of electron charge in a crystal. Thus precise x-ray data can show the way in which valence electrons are distributed in chemical bonds. Such work confirms the fact that there is an increase in electron density between the atoms, corresponding to tetrahedral covalent bonds. Two electrons of opposite spins in each tetrahedral covalent bond would just suffice to explain the x-ray data.

3.2 BAND STRUCTURE

A theoretical calculation of the energy-band structure of silicon is shown in Fig. 3.2. As atoms are brought closer together, isolated individual energy levels interact, as explained before, to give a band of levels. In an isolated atom of silicon the electronic configuration of the valence electrons would be $3s^2 3p^2$, but as electron distributions overlap, these states broaden to give two bands. At internuclear distances corresponding to those in a crystal, the s and p states have mixed together to give hybrid states. These hybrid orbitals are familiar as the sp^3 tetrahedral orbitals of silicon in its state of covalency four. They provide exactly four electronic

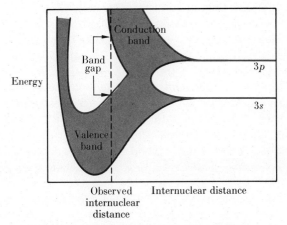

Fig. 3.2. Energy-band structure of silicon.

states per atom, so that in a crystal of Si they are completely filled with the available electrons.

For silicon, diamond, and germanium, we should thus expect the lowest energy band to be filled completely and the upper one to be empty. Hence, these crystals would not be good conductors of electricity like the metals. The lower band is called the *valence band;* the upper band is called the *conduction band,* since any electrons introduced into it should move freely.

The next question is how big is the energy gap or *band gap* between the filled valence band and the conduction band. One way to find this important quantity (we shall mention others later) is to measure the *absorption edge,* that is, the wavelength at onset of optical absorption by the crystal. The absorption edge should correspond quite closely to the energy necessary to transfer an electron from the top of the filled valence band to the bottom of the empty conduction band.

Values of the band gaps for elements with the silicon structure are as follows:

C(diamond) 5.2 eV; Si 1.09 eV; Ge 0.60 eV; Sn 0.08 eV.

These values should be compared with that for NaCl, which is about 10 eV. We note that the band gap in Si and Ge is an order of magnitude less than in an insulating crystal like NaCl.

We mentioned that absorption of light can transfer an electron across the energy gap. Is it not possible that an electron may sometimes acquire enough energy from thermal vibrations of the structure to make such a transition? Consider, for example, a temperature of 1000°K, and apply the Boltzmann distribution formula to the Maxwellian tail of the electron distribution in the valence band. For Si, the ratio of number of electrons thermally excited to number in the valence band would be approximately $\exp(-\epsilon/2kT)$, where ϵ is the band gap. This factor at 1000°K would be $\exp - (1.09 \times 1.602 \times 10^{-12}/1.3805 \times 10^{-16} \times 2 \times 1000) = e^{-6.33} = 10^{-2.75} = 1.78 \times 10^{-3}$. We can therefore predict that an appreciable fraction of electrons (about one in every six hundred) acquire enough thermal energy to jump the band gap. Once in the conduction band they can be accelerated by electric

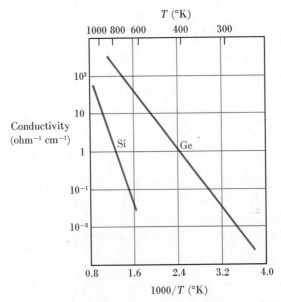

Fig. 3.3. Electrical conductivity of pure silicon and germanium plotted versus reciprocal of temperature in °K.

fields and contribute to the conductivity.[1] We may expect, therefore, that crystals with band gaps of the order of 1 eV or less will show appreciable electronic conductivity at moderately elevated temperatures and this conductivity should increase rapidly with temperature according to an $\exp(-\epsilon/2kT)$ law.

Silicon is therefore a typical *intrinsic semiconductor*. It is called a *semiconductor* because its electrical conductivity ($\sigma = 10^{-2}$ ohm^{-1} cm^{-1} at 20°C) is neither so high as that of a typical metal ($\sigma = 5 \times 10^5$ ohm^{-1} cm^{-1} for Au at 20°C) nor so low as that of a typical insulator ($\sigma = 10^{-12}$ ohm^{-1} cm^{-1} for NaCl at 20°C). The conductivities of purest Si and Ge are plotted in Fig. 3.3 as log σ versus T^{-1}. This plot is linear if

---

[1] The empty spaces in the valence band, called *positive holes*, also contribute to the conductivity, as explained in Section 3.4.

$$\sigma = \sigma_0 \exp\left(\frac{-\epsilon}{2kT}\right) \quad \text{so that} \quad \log \sigma = \log \sigma_0 - \frac{\epsilon}{2kT} \quad (3.1)$$

From the slope of such a plot we obtain a value for the band gap ϵ. The ϵ measured in this way is the *thermal band gap*, and it may not be exactly the same as the *optical band gap* described previously.

It is worth noting that σ for a semiconductor increases with T whereas σ for a metal decreases with increase in T. The mobility term in $\sigma = Ne\mu$ [Eq. (2.1)] is lower at higher T owing to the fact that the vibrations of the atoms in the crystal scatter the electrons more effectively and hence lower their mean free paths. In the case of metals the density of charge carriers (N) increases only slightly with T, so that σ follows the decreasing μ factor. In the case of semiconductors N increases exponentially with T, and such an increase in N far outweighs the decrease of the μ factor.

3.3 HALL EFFECT

You may have been disappointed by the fact that electrical conductivity, which is such a convenient property to measure precisely, depends on the product of two more fundamental parameters (the number of charge carriers and their mobility). You will therefore be glad to know that E. H. Hall discovered in 1879 a galvanomagnetic effect, which permits a convenient separation of these two factors.

We can best understand the Hall effect by considering a typical experimental measurement outlined in Fig. 3.4. A section of crystal to be measured is mounted with electrodes attached so that the flow of current is normal to a fairly strong ($\sim$2000 gauss) magnetic field. The magnetic force on the moving electrons is normal to both the direction of motion and the magnetic field, and hence acts to displace the electron density in the y direction in the figure. As a consequence, an electric potential difference $E_y a$ (where E_y is the field strength, and a the width of the specimen) builds up until it reaches a value high enough to prevent any further transverse displacement of electrons. This potential can be measured with a potentiometer as indicated in the figure.

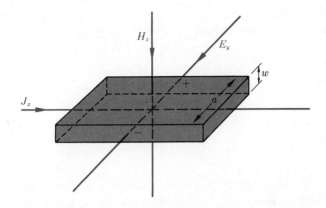

Fig. 3.4. The Hall effect—The magnetic field H_z normal to the current flow J_x produces a transverse electric field E_y. The potential difference $E_y a$ can be measured by attaching leads at $+$ and $-$ to a potentiometer.

The Hall potential is proportional to magnetic field H_z and current J_x, and inversely proportional to the thickness w (measured parallel to H) of the sample. The proportionality factor is the *Hall coefficient* R_H defined by

$$aE_y = \frac{10^{-4} R_H J_x H_z}{w} \tag{3.2}$$

In Eq. (3.2), R_H is in cubic meters per coulomb, when J is in amperes, H in gauss,[2] w in meters, and aE_y in volts. The Hall voltage can be quite appreciable. For example, with a sample of silicon at 20°, $H = 2000$ G, $J = 10^{-3}$ A, and $w = 10^{-3}$ m, aE_y was found to be 0.2 mV.

Suppose the current is made up of electrons flowing parallel to the x axis with velocity v_x. The magnetic field H_z exerts on an electron a force $e v_x H_z$. The electric field E_y required to balance this force would therefore be $E_y = v_x H_z$ (since charge on electron is

---

[2] We use magnetic induction in gauss because of the common use of this unit in work with magnets. The MKS unit of weber m$^{-2} = 10^4$ G, which accounts for the factor of 10^{-4} in our formula.

$-e$). The current density J_x/aw is the product of the number of electrons per unit volume $\times$ their charge $\times$ average velocity, and is given by Eq. (2.1) as $-Nev_x$. Hence, we have from Eq. (3.2)

$$R_H = \frac{-10^4}{Ne} \tag{3.3}$$

Actually, this formula is correct for metals but must be slightly modified for semiconductors to yield

$$R_H = \frac{-10^4(3\pi/8)}{Ne} \tag{3.4}$$

We now see how neatly measurements of Hall coefficients and of conductivities may complement each other. The Hall coefficient R_H depends only on the number of charge carriers N and their charge e, whereas the conductivity $\sigma = Ne\mu$ depends on the product, number of charge carriers $\times$ charge $\times$ mobility. If we measure both R_H and σ, therefore, we can find both N and μ as well as the sign of the charge carrier. For example, $R_H\sigma = -\mu$. In this way we are able to obtain a much better analysis of electronic properties of crystals.

3.4   HOLES AND ELECTRONS

A schematic model for the energy bands of an intrinsic semiconductor like silicon is shown in Fig. 3.5. Let us consider again what happens when an electron is excited from the valence band to the conduction band. We note an important and interesting point, overlooked in our discussions so far. When an electron jumps from valence band to conduction band, it leaves behind a hole in the hitherto filled valence band. As long as the valence band was completely filled, electrons in it could make no contribution to electrical conductivity, since there were no empty states into which they could move. As soon as some holes appear, however, electrons in the top regions of the valence band may find empty states available.

Although we could treat the problem as a movement of electrons in an almost filled band, a different point of view gives a more

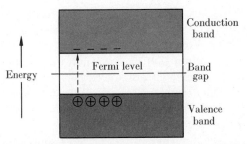

Fig. 3.5. Schematic model of pure silicon as intrinsic semi-conductor. Electrons excited across the band gap into the conduction band leave behind positive holes in the valence band. The Fermi level lies midway between top of valence band and bottom of conduction band.

entrancing physical picture. A hole in a sea of negative electrons is effectively a point of positive charge (2). When an electron jumps from left to right into a hole, it is electrically the same as if a positive electron or positron jumped from right to left. In short, we can treat the motion of electrons in an almost filled valence band as if the holes were positive charges moving in an almost empty hole band. The situation in the valence band thus becomes a sort of mirror image of that in the conduction band. In the latter case, we have a few negative electrons moving in a relatively empty band. In the former case, we have a few positive holes moving in a valence band almost empty of holes.

Electrons and holes, however, besides having opposite charges, differ in another important respect. The mobility of a hole is not the same as that of an electron. We can express this fact in another way by relating mobility μ, which is velocity per unit field, to an effective mass m^* which is a measure of inertia, since $\mu = e/m^*$. Effective mass m^* of a positive hole in a valence band may be quite different from mass of an electron m.[3] Actually, m^* is not constant but depends on temperature, direction in crystal, and other factors.

[3] The reason for this is that positive holes occur near the tops of valence bands, close to the energy gaps. In this region the free electron picture is no longer a good approximation.

For example, in pure silicon m^* ranges from 0.16 to 0.5 m, and in germanium m^* is 0.04 to 0.3 m, where m is electronic mass.

Now that we have become acquainted with positive holes we must go back and admit that the equations we gave before for conductivity and Hall effects were not correct for intrinsic semiconductors. For a material such as silicon, in which both electrons and holes contribute to the properties, we must include terms for both these different current carriers.

The expression for conductivity becomes simply the sum of the contributions from electrons and holes,

$$\sigma = |e|(N_e\mu_e + N_h\mu_h) \qquad (3.5)$$

where $|e|$ indicates the absolute value of electronic charge. In pure intrinsic silicon we should expect $N_e = N_h$, but in other cases the concentrations of oppositely charged carriers may differ considerably from each other. In such instances, we speak of *majority* and *minority* carriers, having higher and lower concentrations, respectively.

When both electrons and holes contribute to the Hall effect, the consequences can be quite complex, since the contributions do not add up but tend to counteract each other because of the opposite signs of the charges. The resultant formula is given by Shockley (3) as:

$$R_H = \frac{-3\pi}{8|e|}\left[\frac{N_e\mu_e^2 - N_h\mu_h^2}{(N_e\mu_e + N_h\mu_h)^2}\right] \qquad (3.6)$$

We shall see that in certain semiconductors the numbers of one carrier (either holes or electrons) may exceed those of the other by a large factor. In such case the general formulas of the Eqs. (3.5) and (3.6) reduce to the simpler formulas of Eqs. (2.1) and (3.4).

3.5   DOPING OF SILICON

There is an interesting analogy between the behavior of an intrinsic semiconductor like silicon and that of a weakly dissociated solvent like water (4). Water ionizes as

$$H_2O \rightleftharpoons H^+ + OH^-$$

with dissociation constant

$$K_w = [H^+][OH^-]$$

where the square brackets denote concentrations. In the same way we can write for the excitation of an electron to a conduction band in silicon, leaving a hole in the valence band,

$$Si \rightarrow e^- + h^+$$

with an equilibrium constant,

$$K_i = [e][h]$$

In pure intrinsic silicon,

$$[e] = [h] = K_i^{1/2}$$

We often write $[e] = n$ and $[h] = p$ to indicate explicitly the negative and positive nature of these charge carriers.

If we try to carry this analogy further, what would correspond to the solution of a weak base or weak acid in water? The answer is, the solution in the silicon structure of impurity atoms with either more or less valence electrons than the four of silicon. For example, atoms such as As, Sb, and P would have five valence electrons, and atoms such as B and In would have only three valence electrons.

The situation that results from substitution of such foreign atoms in the silicon structure is shown in Fig. 3.6a. In terms of the simple band model, we can see that four electrons of a P atom can be accommodated in the normal valence band, but the fifth electron must go into a higher-energy state. In fact this energy state lies only 0.012 eV below the conduction band. It will therefore be easy to excite electrons from these impurity levels into the conduction band. We then obtain a semiconductor with a greatly enhanced number of conduction electrons. We call this an *n-type* semiconductor because the majority current carriers are (negative) electrons. We call a doping atom such as P, or As, which can give electrons to the conduction band, a *donor*. We call the extra energy levels introduced into the band gap below the conduction band,

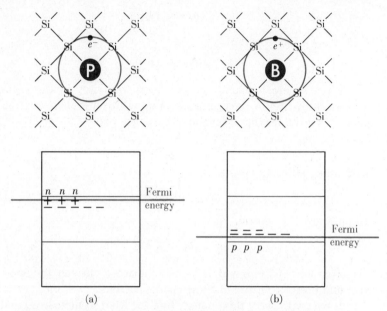

Fig. 3.6. **(a) Doping of silicon with electron donors (P, for example) leads to electrons in conduction band and *n*-type silicon.** **(b) Doping with electron acceptors (B, for example) leads to positive holes in conduction band and *p*-type silicon.**

donor levels. When the electron is excited from donor level into conduction band, we say that the electron has been *dissociated* from its donor site.

The fundamental equilibrium expression, $K_i = [e][h] = np$ still holds, but now $n \gg p$. The solution of donor atoms in silicon is analogous to the solution of a weak base in water, which would greatly increase the concentration of OH^- ions and decrease that of H^+ ions.

If the doping atom was deficient in valence electrons, like B or In, we would have the situation shown in Fig. 3.6b. There would be an unfilled hole in the tetrahedral sp^3 bonds about the B atom. The result of this would be to introduce a new level into the band gap somewhat above the top of the valence band (in the case of B in Si actually only 0.01 eV above). Such a level can act as an *acceptor level*, since electrons can jump from the valence band to the acceptor. This process leaves a positive hole in the valence band, and can therefore be considered a dissociation of a positive hole p which was originally trapped at an acceptor-atom site. The positive holes in the valence band can conduct current and the conductivity of the crystal will be greatly enhanced over that of pure silicon. We then have a typical *p-type* semiconductor, in which the majority carriers are positive holes and the number of electrons in the conduction band is repressed in accord with the equilibrium expression. This situation is analogous to the dissociation of a weak acid in water, which greatly enhances the concentration of H^+ ions and represses that of OH^- ions.

In writing the reaction of ionization of a donor or acceptor, we use the principle that the lowest-energy state is that which preserves local electrical neutrality. Thus we can insert a neutral P atom in place of a neutral Si atom. The extra electron, which cannot find a place in the valence band, is attached to this center in much the same way as the electron in the Bohr hydrogen atom is attached to the central proton. The orbit of an electron about such a P^+ center is believed to have quite a large diameter, since the energy of interaction is reduced by the effective dielectric constant D of the medium. Instead of the formula of the Bohr theory for the radius of the ground state of the hydrogen atom,

$$r_0 = \frac{h^2}{4\pi^2 m e^2} = 0.529 \text{ Å}$$

we have

$$r = D r_0$$

For example, with the bulk $D = 11.8$ of silicon, the Bohr orbit would be 12.4 Å in diameter, extending over about 50 atoms.[4] N. F. Mott coined the descriptive phrase "great swollen atoms" to describe these centers in the solid state.

We can conveniently write the ionization as a freeing of the electron from the center

---

[4] The value of D close to a charged center may differ from the bulk D, but our general conclusions are still valid.

$$(P^+ \ldots e^-) \rightarrow P^+ + e^-$$

In case of an acceptor site, for example, boron, we would have

$$(B^- \ldots h^+) \rightarrow B^- + h^+$$

Not all dopants in silicon enter into substitutional solid solution. Some small atoms such as lithium can enter interstitial sites in the structure, and can then ionize as donors,

$$Li \rightarrow Li^+ + e^-$$

In Table 3.1 we summarize ionization energies of various solutes in both silicon and germanium crystals.

Table 3.1   Ionization Energies of Solutes in Silicon and Germanium (in eV)

	In Silicon	In Germanium
Donors		
Li^+	0.0093	0.033
P^+	0.012	0.045
As^+	0.0127	0.049
Sb^+	0.0096	0.039
Acceptors		
B^-	0.0104	0.045
As^-	0.0102	0.057
In^-	0.0112	0.16
Cu^-	0.04	0.49

3.6   FERMI LEVELS IN SEMICONDUCTORS

Let us consider first an intrinsic semiconductor without impurity levels. Then the equilibrium concentration of electrons in the conduction band is given by

$$n = N_c \exp\left(\frac{E_F - E_c}{kT}\right) \tag{3.7}$$

N_c is the density of states in the conduction band, or more explicitly, in the lowest part of the conduction band, and E_c is the energy at the same level. This expression is the classical form of the Fermi–Dirac distribution function, which we are allowed to use because $n \ll N_c$, only a few electrons being in the conduction band. We can also use this classical approximation for the concentration of holes in the valence band,

$$p = N_v \exp\left(\frac{E_v - E_F}{kT}\right) \tag{3.8}$$

where E_v is the energy level of the top of the valence band and N_v is the density of states in that region.

We know that in the intrinsic case, $n = p$, so that from Eqs. (3.7) and (3.8),

$$N_c \exp\left(\frac{E_F - E_c}{kT}\right) = N_v \exp\left(\frac{E_v - E_F}{kT}\right)$$

On taking logarithms and rearrangement this yields

$$E_F = \frac{E_v + E_c}{2} + \frac{1}{2} kT \ln\left(\frac{N_v}{N_c}\right) \tag{3.9}$$

Since $N_v \approx N_c$, the position of the Fermi energy in an intrinsic semiconductor lies almost exactly midway between the top of the valence band and the bottom of the conduction band, as shown in Fig. 3.5.

If we introduce donor and (or) acceptor levels into the crystal, the level of the Fermi energy will change, since the equilibrium distribution of n and p must adjust so as to preserve electrical neutrality at all times. The condition for electrical neutrality is

$$n + (N_A - p_A) = p + (N_D - n_D)$$

where p_A is the concentration of holes on acceptor centers (that is, concentration of unionized acceptors) and n_D is the concentration of electrons on donor centers. The calculation of the level of the Fermi energy is a special problem in each case since it depends on the positions of the various donor and acceptor levels, the temperature, and the band gap. In an n-type semiconductor the level will usually lie between the donor levels and the conduction band.

In a p-type semiconductor it will lie between the valence band and the acceptor levels. In a metal, as we saw in Chapter 2, the Fermi energy level lies near the top of the filled states in the conduction band.

Suppose two different crystals with the Fermi energies at different levels are brought into contact. We can do this by physically bringing together two separate crystals or by treating a crystal so that one part is differently doped from another. We now recall that the Fermi energy is identical with the electrochemical potential of electrons. Electrons must flow from high electrochemical potential to low electrochemical potential as long as any difference in electrochemical potential exists. Such a flow occurs until an electric field is set up which effectively counterbalances the original difference in the Fermi levels. Thus if two crystals are brought into contact, electrons will flow from one section to the other until the Fermi energy (electrochemical potential) is uniform throughout the specimen.

3.7   THE p-n JUNCTION

Suppose we bring a piece of n-type silicon into contact with a piece of p-type silicon. We then have a *p-n junction*. A schematic diagram of the energy bands is shown in Fig. 3.7. The band system must be distorted in order to secure a uniformity in Fermi level across the junction.

When contact is made, excess electrons in the conduction band on the n side spill over the steep gradient in E_F and positive holes on the p side move over into the valence band of the n-type silicon. This interchange persists until a sufficient electrical potential is built up in a double layer to prevent further charge transfer across the boundary.

Such a p-n junction has a pronounced rectifier action, that is, its ability to conduct an electrical current is different in the two opposite directions. At equilibrium the flow of electrons from p to n side across the barrier must equal the reverse flow of electrons from n to p. A similar equality must hold for the flows of holes. Some of the electrons in the n region acquire enough energy to surmount

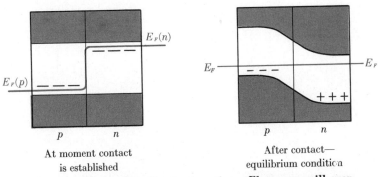

At moment contact
is established

After contact—
equilibrium condition

Fig. 3.7. Formation of a *p-n* junction. Electrons spill over gradient of electrochemical potential E_F from the *n* to the *p* side, until the + charge on *n* side and the − charge on *p* side set up an electrostatic potential sufficient to equalize E_F across the junction at equilibrium.

the electrostatic barrier. This current is called I_f. In the *p* region some of the electrons are thermally excited from the valence band to the conduction band and these contribute a current I_g. Thus at equilibrium, $I_g = I_f$. Suppose we now connect a battery across the terminals of the *p-n* junction so as to apply a positive potential to the *p* side. The result is to lower greatly the electrical potential barrier between the two regions. Now the electrons can move from *n* to *p* region without surmounting the high electrostatic barrier that previously impeded them. In the same way holes can move much more freely from *p* to *n*. Note that electrons move spontaneously down Fermi potential hills, whereas positive holes move spontaneously up such hills. We are thus using the Fermi energy (electrochemical potential of electrons) to describe the flows of both electrons and holes. The position of the valence and conduction bands and the gradient of the Fermi energy under forward bias are shown in Fig. 3.8a. As we increase the voltage in this condition of *forward bias*, we therefore obtain a rapid increase in the current carried across the junction, as shown in Fig. 3.8b.

On the other hand, suppose the applied electric potential is reversed; this condition is called *reverse bias*. In this case the

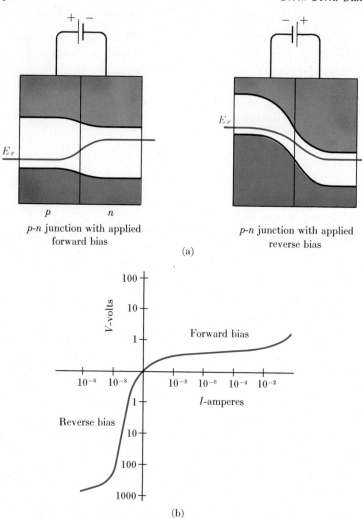

p-n junction with applied
forward bias

p-n junction with applied
reverse bias

(a)

(b)

Fig. 3.8.   The *p-n* junction as a rectifier: (a) location of bands
and Fermi energy level under forward and reverse bias, (b) the
current-voltage characteristic.

height of the potential barrier is increased still further over the un-biased state. The forward flow I_f of electrons and holes is reduced to an almost negligible amount. The thermally generated flow is somewhat increased, but this is small in any case. The positions of the bands in this condition of *reverse bias* are also shown in Fig. 3.8a, with the corresponding I-V characteristic in Fig. 3.8b.

We can see at once that the *p-n* junction can act as a rectifier, passing current readily in one direction but not in the other, and thus can convert an ac to a dc current. We considered in this case that the *p* and *n* sections were equally doped, but by appropriately adjusting the equilibrium concentrations of electrons and holes it is possible to enhance the rectifier action still further. Some of the most important rectifiers used in industry are now based on silicon *p-n* junctions of this type.

3.8   THE TRANSISTOR

Although the rectifier action of the *p-n* junction was extremely important, the real breakthrough in solid state electronics came with the invention of an amplifier, the transistor, by Shockley, Bardeen, and Brattain in 1948. This is the device that has replaced the vacuum tube in countless electronic applications.

We can see how it is possible to secure amplification by studying a typical *p-n-p junction transistor* shown in Fig. 3.9. A thin layer of *n*-type silicon separates two *p*-type regions. In Fig. 3.9b the energy bands are shown in the absence of any bias applied to either side. In operation as a transistor, a positive bias is applied to the left side and a negative bias to the right as shown in Fig. 3.9a. These applied potentials alter the energy bands to configurations like those shown in Fig. 3.9c. In consideration of the potential we always recall our convention in which positive holes flow uphill and electrons flow downhill along electron electrochemical potential surfaces.

When the emitter junction J_E is biased positively with respect to the base electrode, positive holes are emitted (or injected) into

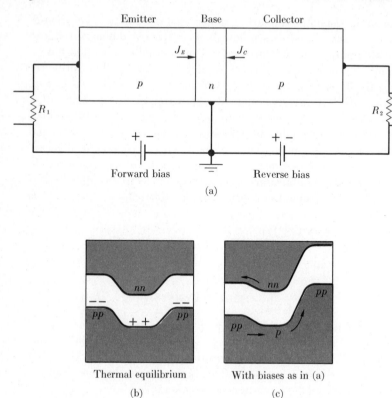

Fig. 3.9. **A *p-n-p* junction transistor in operation as a power amplifier.**

the *n*-type region of the base[5] and electrons are injected into the *p*-type region of the emitter. The forward bias greatly promotes the flow of charge carriers in the directions cited. The emitter region is more heavily doped than the base region and thus has a considerably higher conductivity. Hence, the current flow across the junction J_E is predominantly positive holes. The junction J_c between collector and base carries a reverse bias. The base region

---

[5] Or we might say that electrons are attracted out of the *n*-type region.

is made very thin so that most of the positive holes can diffuse across it without recombining with electrons n. The positive holes that reach the collector flow easily into it and across it under the conditions of negative bias at J_c. Thus, it becomes possible to inject a current of holes from the emitter and to have 90% or more of it flow through to the collector. (Since the emitter and collector are p-type material, the current carried by positive holes is predominant in this example, although it would of course be possible also to have a n-p-n type junction transistor in which this situation was reversed.)

The emitter-base junction J_E is a region of low impedance, since under the condition of forward bias, holes have been injected into it. On the other hand, the collector-base junction J_c is a region of high impedance, since under the condition of reverse bias, holes have been removed from it. If we arrange the resistances of the junctions suitably, by adjusting the concentrations of doping material, and also adjust the biases properly, we can get a flow of current through the junction from a low resistance R_1 region to a high resistance R_2 region. The voltage amplification will thus be given approximately by the ratio R_2/R_1 (since $E = IR$). The power is the product IE and it is also amplified by the device. By suitable arrangement one can also obtain current amplification. Thus the junction transistor can serve as an amplifying device, similar in many respects to the ordinary triode tube used in old-fashioned electronics.

3.9 GROWING SILICON CRYSTALS

The expansion of solid state electronics has created an enormous demand for large single crystals of silicon and germanium. (There would be a demand for diamond also if there was a way to fill it.) For some purposes crystals of ultrahigh purity are required, and for others, crystals doped with carefully controlled concentrations of specific additives. It is possible to design entire electronic circuits within individual single crystals of silicon and germanium by appropriate doping of different regions, either by diffusion or by inserting dopant atoms by ion bombardment or other injection methods. This technique has been somewhat inaccurately called "molecular electronics."

These semiconductor crystals are almost always grown from a melt with a composition close to that finally desired. In this way complications due to nonuniform composition can be minimized. The principal problem in growing large crystals is control of the temperature gradients that must exist in the system. Suppose we have a liquid melt with a solid crystal in contact with it. As more liquid freezes to solid, the enthalpy of fusion ΔH_f is liberated as heat and must be removed from the system.

A clever technique much used in earlier days was devised by Gustav Tammann about 1920. The powdered material was placed in a crucible having the shape shown in Fig. 3.10a. After the material was melted, the crucible was slowly lowered out of the high-temperature zone of the furnace. As the narrow bottom of the crucible cooled, crystal nuclei formed and gradually grew so as to fill this entire region. It was usually possible to fix the cooling rate so that only one particular single crystal filled the bottom tip of the crucible. Then as the crucible was slowly lowered from the furnace, the melt crystallized at the surface of this individual crystal seed and gradually a large single crystal filled the entire crucible.

Most silicon crystals are now made by the Czochralski method, called *crystal pulling* (Fig. 3.10b). A seed crystal is held on a vertical shaft and brought into contact with the surface of the melt. The thermal gradients are arranged so that new crystal is formed at the interface. The crystal is slowly rotated and pulled upward from the melt. Crystals as large as 50 cm in diameter have been pulled by this technique. These crystals can be sliced into thin sections and used in rectifiers and other solid state devices.

As demands for control of impurities grew more stringent, crystal growers wanted to eliminate the crucible altogether, since it was often the major source of contamination. An ingenious method now widely applied in industry is the *floating-zone technique* (Fig. 3.10c). A solid ingot of polycrystalline material is melted by induction heating only at its top end and a new single crystal is drawn from that end. The molten section is just long enough to

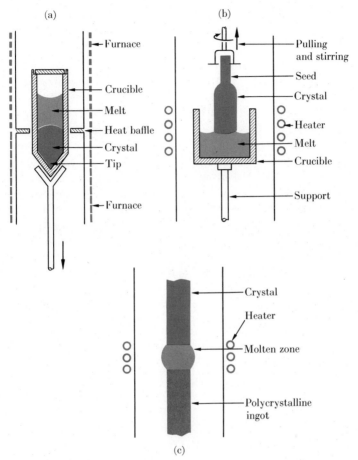

(a)   (b)

Furnace

Crucible

Melt

Heat baffle

Crystal

Tip

Furnace

Pulling
and stirring

Seed

Crystal

Heater

Melt

Crucible

Support

Crystal

Heater

Molten zone

Polycrystalline
ingot

(c)

Fig. 3.10.   Methods for growing single crystals.

support itself by surface tension between its parent, the polycrystalline rod, and its offspring, the monocrystal being pulled.   Completely automated floating-zone machines are now widely used for
growing silicon and germanium crystals.

3.10   ZONE REFINING

Even after a crystal is grown, it is possible to purify it further. You are familiar with the process of fractional crystallization as a means of purifying materials.   It is based on an unequal distribution of impurities between liquid and crystal phases.   Chemists use it routinely under the name of "recrystallization."   William Pfann at Bell Telephone Laboratories devised a sort of continuous recrystallization, called *zone refining*, that has pushed the limits of purity in crystals several orders of magnitude beyond anything hitherto considered imaginable.   It is now fairly easy to obtain silicon crystals with less than one part in 10^{10} of impurity.   Like many inventions, zone refining seemed almost obvious after it had once been done, but it required a flash of genius to think of it the first time.

The zone refining process is illustrated schematically in Fig. 3.11a.   The construction of laboratory equipment for zone refining with an unsupported floating zone is shown in Fig. 3.11b.

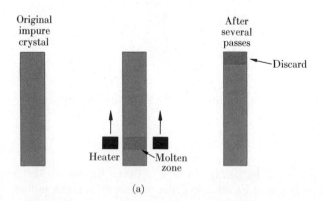

(a)

Fig. 3.11.   (a) Zone refining of a crystal rod.   (b) View of large vacuum chamber equipped for vertical unsupported floating-zone refining with internal heater.   [Parr (5).]

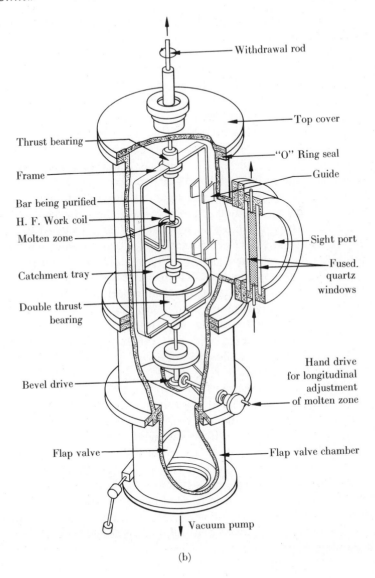

Withdrawal rod

Top cover

Thrust bearing

"O" Ring seal

Frame

Guide

Bar being purified

H. F. Work coil

Molten zone

Sight port

Catchment tray

Fused. quartz windows

Double thrust bearing

Hand drive for longitudinal adjustment of molten zone

Bevel drive

Flap valve

Flap valve chamber

Vacuum pump

(b)

Consider a solid in equilibrium with a zone of melt. The distribution coefficient of an impurity between liquid and solid is defined by $K = C_l/C_s$. Generally, K is considerably greater than unity, since the solubility of impurity in the liquid is higher than in the solid phase. Suppose now the molten zone is moved through the bar of crystal, starting at $x = 0$. This can be done easily with an induction heater in the form of a ring enclosing the crystal bar. Initially, the crystal has a uniform concentration of impurity C_0. At $x = 0$, the first melt therefore has this same C_0. As the zone moves (x increases) the melt reaches an impurity concentration higher than the initial value. As the zone of melt moves along x it takes in liquid of composition C_0 and leaves behind solid with a lower impurity composition. Impurity accumulates in the moving liquid zone until it reaches a concentration of KC_0 at some distance $x = a$ from the origin. Further motion of the zone cannot result in further purification, but it does tend to produce *zone leveling*, that is, a uniformity in composition of the region traversed. This process of zone leveling is also of great practical importance, since it is the most convenient way to produce a uniform composition in a crystal. After the first "pass," the heater can be returned to the origin (without remelting anything to be sure), and the zone melting repeated. Several passes usually suffice to sweep most of the original impurities out of the first region of crystal.

Many of the important industrial advances of solid state electronics have been based on zone-refining techniques. The method is of course not limited to semiconductor crystals such as Si and Ge. For instance, it is now being widely used to purify organic crystals, especially those wanted for the study of phosphorescence and luminescence, in which even traces of impurities may have startling effects (6). It is also used for purifying metal crystals and some of the most fascinating recent work in the chemistry of metals has shown that reactions of metals may be profoundly influenced by small traces of impurities below the one part in a million level. For example, chromium is usually a hard, brittle metal, but when prepared in ultrapure form it is so ductile that it can be drawn into fine wires. In impure chromium, the impurities segregate at intercrystalline boundaries to form brittle films that destroy the ductility of the metal.

REFERENCES

(1) G. H. Wannier, *Solid State Theory* (Cambridge: Cambridge University Press, 1959).

(2) A. H. Wilson, *Semi-conductors and Metals* (Cambridge University Press, 1939), pp. 8–10.

(3) W. Shockley, *Electrons and Holes in Semiconductors* (Princeton, N.J.: Van Nostrand, 1950), pp. 204–217.

(4) C. S. Fuller, "Some Analogies between Semiconductors and Electrolyte Solutions," *Record Chemical Progress* 17, 75 (1956).

(5) N. L. Parr, *Zone Refining and Allied Techniques* (London: George Newnes, 1960).

(6) H. Schildknecht, *Zone Melting* (New York: Academic Press, 1966), pp. 170–198.

IV

Steel

About 550 A.D. a Persian poet, Aus ben Hajar, wrote a song of praise to the blade of his sword: "It is water with wavy streaks glistening. It is a pool with wind gliding over its surface. The smith has worked a grain like a trail of small black ants in the still soft metal." This was one of the famous *Damascus blades*, forged from a cake of *wootz*, a high carbon (1.5 to 2.0% C) Indian steel. Not until 1821 did European armorers learn how to make these blades of oriental damask. The secret was not in the forging, but in the melting and heat treatment of wootz to obtain the exact mixture of steel and iron carbide (the little black ants) [see Smith (1)]. Like most problems of steel, this one was concerned with the properties of the iron-carbon system. Therefore, we shall look first at the structure of pure iron and then consider how it can dissolve carbon in the solid state.

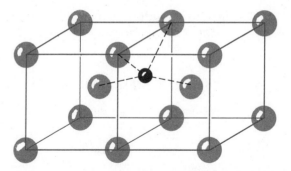

Fig. 4.1. Two adjacent unit cells of body-centered cubic (bcc) iron, showing a tetrahedral interstitial site occupied by a carbon atom.

4.1 CRYSTAL STRUCTURE OF IRON

The stable form of iron at room temperature is called α-iron. It crystallizes in the bcc structure shown in Fig. 4.1 with $a_0 = 2.861$ Å at 20°C. There are two atoms in the unit cell. Each atom has eight nearest neighbors, compared to twelve in the closest-packed structures, fcc and hcp.

Below 760°C iron is ferromagnetic—a piece of iron can be permanently magnetized by an applied magnetic field. Above that temperature, called its *Curie point*, iron is no longer ferromagnetic, although the bcc structure has not changed. It is paramagnetic— being attracted into a magnetic field but no longer capable of becoming a permanent magnet. This paramagnetic iron used to be called β-iron, but is now called simply paramagnetic α-iron. I mention this fact so that you will not keep looking for β-iron when you see α, γ, and δ.

At 906°C transition occurs to γ-iron which has a different crystal structure, fcc. On further heating, a rather unusual reversal takes place at 1401°C, back to the bcc structure, now called δ-iron. This structure is stable up to the melting point of 1530°C.

The change from bcc α-Fe to fcc γ-Fe is accompanied by a small decrease in volume, 0.001 cm³ g⁻¹. Hence, an increase in pressure would lower the transition temperature of αFe $\rightarrow$ γFe. At about 10,000 kg cm^{-2}, it is down as far as 800°C.

4.2 ELECTRONIC STRUCTURE OF IRON

The electronic configuration of an isolated iron atom is

$$\boxed{1s^2 2s^2 2p^6 3s^2 3p^6} \; 3d^6 4s^2$$

Argon core

Thus iron is one of the *transition metals*, in which a partly filled shell of d electrons results in characteristic properties such as variable valence, colored ions, and paramagnetism. An exact quantum mechanical theory of these metals has not yet been worked out. In iron, for example, the problem of how to bond together atoms with eight valence electrons, all of which may contribute to the cohesion of the metal, is much too difficult to solve by present methods. Thus, we can present a plausible but by no means exact picture of the bonding in iron and similar transition metals.

As the isolated atoms are brought together, the sharp energy levels for electrons in atoms broaden into energy bands. We should expect to get a $3d$ band and a $4s$ band. The $3d$ electrons, on the average, are more closely held to the nucleus than are the $4s$. Hence, $3d$ orbitals of adjacent atoms overlap less than $4s$. Consequently, the band that arises from $3d$ levels will be more narrow than the $4s$ band. A schematic graph of the density of states in these two bands is shown in Fig. 4.2. The energies of the bands overlap each other to a considerable extent. Therefore, when we pour the available electrons into the two bands, they will reach the same level in both bands, and each one is consequently only partly filled. We find that there are 0.22 electrons per atom in the $4s$ band and 7.78 electrons per atom in the $3d$ band. It is impossible to calculate these figures theoretically. They are estimated from the experimental magnetic properties of iron.

Several complications in this oversimplified band model were soon noticed. Since the $3d$ and $4s$ bands overlap, an electron usually can be neither purely d nor purely s in its wave properties. An appropriate wave function might be some hybrid of d and s types.

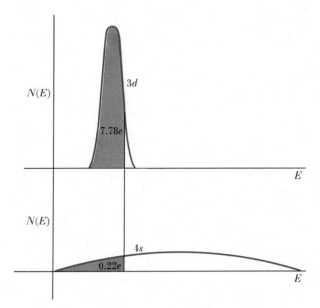

Fig. 4.2.   Density of states in 3d and 4s bands of iron.

The situation is even more complicated by the fact that several low-lying excited states of atomic iron exist, at energies above the ground state which are smaller than the width of the band arising from the ground states.   Thus these excited states must certainly be included before we can write down an appropriate wave function for an electron in iron.   For example, the ground state of the iron atom is $d^6s^2(^5D)$ but the states $d^7s(^5F)$, $d^6sp(^7D)$, and $d^8(^3F)$ are all within 5 eV of the ground state.

In view of these low-lying excited states of the iron atom, Pauling proposed a *bond model* for metallic iron which differed from the band model in some respects (2).   He began by pointing out an analogy with the carbon atom.   The ground state of carbon is $s^2p^2(^3P)$; this state would lead to compounds of bivalent carbon such as CH_2 and CO.   The quadrivalent sp^3 excited state of carbon (^5S) lies 7 eV above the ground state.   Nevertheless, carbon usually displays a covalence of four because the extra energy required to promote electrons to the sp^3 valence state is more than regained by the increased energy of formation of four strong tetrahedral bonds. Now, if an iron atom was excited to a configuration $3d^54s4p^2$, it could use six electrons to make electron-pair bonds with other iron atoms and have two unpaired electrons in its two remaining orbitals. These two unpaired electrons would correspond to a magnetic moment of 2 Bohr magnetons per atom, whereas the observed value is 2.2 for iron. As of now, it is not possible to decide by either theory or experiment whether the band model or the Pauling bond model gives the better representation of metallic iron. We can regard the two approaches as complementary ways of describing the electronic structure of a transition metal.

We should add a word about the way in which magnetic moments determine the number of unpaired electrons. A spinning electron acts as a little magnet, whose magnetic moment μ is $eh/4\pi m = \mu_B$, that is, one Bohr magneton. If the axis of a magnet makes an angle θ to an external field H, the energy of interaction is $V = -\mu H \cos \theta$. When the field becomes strong enough, the magnet lines up in the field direction so that $\theta \to 0$, and $V \to -\mu H$. This limiting effect at high fields gives the *saturation moment* from which the number of unpaired electron spins can be determined. If an electron or atom in a molecule is paired with one of opposite spin, the resultant magnetic moment cancels to zero. On the other hand, the magnetic moments due to unpaired spins add to give a net moment which can be calculated from the saturation moment. If there are n unpaired spins the resultant moment will be $[n(n + 2)]^{1/2}$ Bohr magnetons. Thus, paramagnetism is essentially an atomic property. The ferromagnetism of iron, however, which we shall discuss later, is a property of the solid as a whole, being due to alignment of all the elementary atomic magnets in distinct domains throughout the crystal. So long as this alignment persists, the piece of crystal will act as a permanent magnet.

4.3   SOLUTION OF CARBON IN IRON

The electronic theory of metals has not yet been developed to such an extent that we can predict theoretically all the properties of iron and steel. Yet steel is the most important of all structural materials and metallurgists have acquired a deep understanding of its properties from experimental and technical studies. We shall, therefore, consider some of the most basic information about steel from the experimental point of view.

Figure 4.3 shows a portion of the iron-carbon phase diagram, extending from pure iron to the iron carbide Fe_3C, known in metallurgy as *cementite*. Cementite has an orthorhombic crystal structure and is ferromagnetic with a Curie point at 210°C. You will notice two sets of lines on the diagram, solid lines for equilibria between iron and graphite and dashed lines for iron and cementite. Actually, cementite is metastable with respect to iron and graphite over the entire region shown. Nevertheless, its equilibria with iron are readily studied since its lifetime in the various steel compositions is long compared to the time needed to make the measurements on the system.

The solid solution of carbon in fcc γ-Fe is called *austenite*, and the solution in bcc α-Fe is called simply *α-ferrite*.

The phase diagram shows the distinction between alloys called *steels* and those called *cast irons*. Any composition below 2 wt % (8.7 atom %) carbon can be heated until a solid solution is obtained. In this condition the alloy can be hot rolled, pressed, drawn, or formed by other mechanical operations. It is a *steel*. Compositions above 2 wt % carbon belong to the class of *cast irons*. No heat treatment can bring them into a solid state which can be readily worked. They are therefore formed by casting from the molten state.

At the eutectoid[1] temperature of 723°C, fcc γ-Fe dissolves up to 3.6 atom % carbon, whereas bcc α-Fe at this temperature can dissolve only 0.1 atom %. At first such a difference seems unreasonable, because the fcc structure is more closely packed than the bcc. Closer examination of these structures shows, however, that

---

[1] In a solid-liquid equilibrium diagram for two components A and B, the two $T-C$ curves, for lowering fusion temperature of A by added B, and of B by added A, intersect at the *eutectic* point. This would be the minimum fusion point for that system. In a system containing only solid phases, a similar minimum is called a *eutectoid*. At the eutectoid point, one solid phase (γ) is transformed into two other solid phases ($\alpha + Fe_3C$).

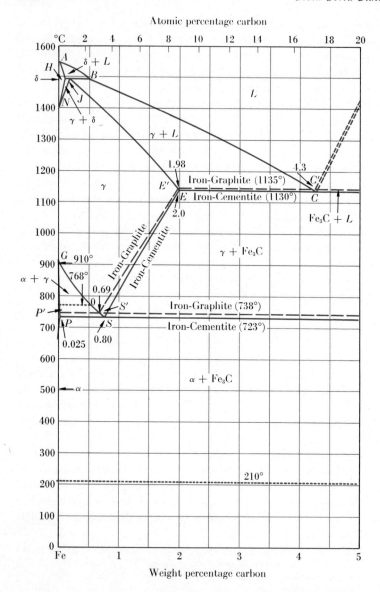

Atomic percentage carbon

Fig. 4.3.   Portion of the iron-carbon phase diagram.   [Austin (3).]

the most spacious sites for a dissolved carbon atom are larger in the fcc than in the bcc structure. In fcc iron the centers of the largest voids are surrounded octahedrally by six equidistant iron atoms. The distance between the center of a carbon atom dissolved in one of these sites to the center of a neighboring iron atom would be 1.82 Å. In the bcc structure the largest available interstitial voids are tetrahedral sites, with the centers of surrounding iron atoms lying only 1.61 Å from the center of the interstitial site. This *interstitial site* was illustrated in Fig. 4.1. Thus, when a carbon atom dissolves in solid iron, by entering one of these interstitial sites, it will be considerably more squeezed in the bcc than in the fcc structure.

We can see this effect in the heats of solution of C(graphite) in iron at the $\alpha \rightleftharpoons \gamma$ transition temperature:

C(graphite) + Fe(fcc) $\rightarrow$ austenite $\Delta \bar{H}$ = 10.8 kcal mole^{-1}

C(graphite) + Fe(bcc) $\rightarrow$ α-ferrite $\Delta \bar{H}$ = 20.0 kcal mole^{-1}

Both heats of solution are quite endothermic, but the $\Delta \bar{H}$ in the bcc is about 9.2 kcal mole^{-1} more so than that in the fcc.

4.4 MARTENSITE

If austenite is cooled slowly below the eutectoid temperature of 723°C, it decomposes to α-ferrite and cementite, the two "stable" phases. If it is cooled rapidly, however, a metastable phase called *martensite* may be formed. Martensite contains carbon atoms in the interstitial sites of a body-centered arrangement of iron atoms, but, unlike α-ferrite, its structure is not exactly cubic. In Fig. 4.1 suppose the interstitial carbon is placed exactly at the center of a cube face and the two nearest neighbor (body-centered) iron atoms are pushed slightly away. The structure is thereby expanded along one axis (*c*), in order to accommodate better the carbon atoms. Thus, the crystal system is now *tetragonal*. The axial ratio, c/a, increases almost linearly with the carbon content, to a maximum of 1.08 in the highest carbon steels.

Martensite is the hardest constituent in quenched steels. One reason for the overall hardness of such steels is the local stress produced around the tiny crystals of martensite, because they have tetragonal structures that cannot be fitted into the surrounding cubic material without causing considerable distortion in their immediate neighborhoods.

The conversion of austenite to martensite when a steel is quenched is an example of a rate process in the solid state that does not involve diffusion. Such *martensitic transformations* have therefore been intensively studied as examples of a type of solid state reaction that cannot be found in fluid systems (4). The speed of the reaction is remarkable. Once a nucleus of martensite is formed, it will grow to its final form, a small needlelike crystal, in a time of the order of 10^{-7} sec. If an amplifier is placed near the specimen, one can hear each little crystallite emit an audible click as it is formed. The rate of growth of the crystallite is of the order of the speed of sound in the solid. The rate is independent of temperature, even down to 4°K. The mechanism appears to be the propagation of a shear wave through the crystal structure, transforming a small region of crystal from fcc to body-centered tetragonal.

When steel is hardened by heat treatment, the cycle of temperature and time is chosen so as to obtain a large proportion of martensite in its microstructure.

4.5 PEARLITE

If, instead of quenching a homogeneous austenite steel rapidly, we maintain it between 570° and 720°C, the solid solution decomposes slowly to yield the "stable" products α-ferrite and cementite. The rate of formation of the new phases under these conditions is quite slow and is usually controlled by the rate of diffusion of carbon atoms to the interface of the growing cementite crystallites. The photomicrograph in Fig. 4.4a shows the typical appearance of the two phases formed by decomposition of austenite: a lamellar structure of alternate bands of cementite and α-ferrite. This composite material is of course not a "structure" in the crystallographic sense. Yet its appearance is so characteristic that it has been given a special name, *pearlite*.

The mechanism of formation of pearlite is suggested in Fig. 4.4b. First, a nucleus of Fe₃C is formed and then carbon diffuses through the matrix of austenite and the Fe_3C deposit extends rapidly in a lateral direction and grows more slowly in depth. As the carbon is depleted by formation of Fe_3C, an α-ferrite nucleus can form adjacent to the Fe_3C phase. As this α-ferrite deposit extends along the layer of Fe_3C, it rejects its excess carbon, building up the carbon concentration in an adjacent layer and favoring the formation of a new nucleus of Fe_3C. The lamellar structure of pearlite can be explained as the consequence of an alternating rise and fall in concentration of dissolved carbon, governed by the nucleation and diffusion-controlled growth of the two phases.

Fig. 4.4a. Photomicrograph at 1250 X of pearlite formed from austenite. (U.S. Steel Corporation Research Center.)

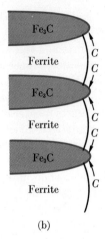

(b)

Fig. 4.4b. Diffusion of carbon atoms through α-ferrite to form pearlitic structure.

4.6 MECHANICAL PROPERTIES OF STEEL

The variety of different stable and metastable phases in the iron-carbon system, the different physical forms of the microstructures in which they can occur, and the changes caused by heat treatment of these systems, all help to explain the astonishing variety of mechanical properties that can be achieved in steels. When a metal part is specified in an industrial design, the engineer must be able to estimate how it will stand up to the stresses of actual use. Thus the mechanical properties of solid materials are often their most important specifications (5).

When a piece of metal is subject to stress below a certain limit, it will deform *elastically*, that is, when the stress is removed, it will return to its original dimensions. When the applied stress exceeds a certain *elastic limit*, however, a *plastic deformation* is produced, which is not completely recovered upon removal of stress. There remains a certain plastic deformation at zero load, called the *permanent set*. We make use of this plastic deformation of metals every time we form them into a desired shape by stamping, drawing, pressing, or forging. Once the metal is formed, however, we prefer to have it keep its equilibrium shape by behaving elastically and not plastically under the stress of normal usage.

Metals are usually tested by being subjected to a tensile or pulling stress. The elongation produced is called the *strain*. In a typical tensile test a metal specimen, somewhat thicker or wider at the ends, is clamped in the jaws of a machine which can apply tensile stress and at the same time record both stress and extension of the specimen. A load is applied at a constant rate. The elongation L of the specimen (strain) is measured as a function of applied load S, and is plotted automatically to give a load-strain curve such as the one in Fig. 4.5.

There is at first a line or section of a curve in accord with an equation

$$L = YS \qquad (4.1)$$

where Y is called *Young's Modulus*. If the stress is removed at any point along this linear curve, the strain will return to zero, since the elastic limit has not been exceeded. At point A, however, corresponding to the elastic limit S_E, the stress-strain curve departs from linearity and strain increases more rapidly than would be cal-

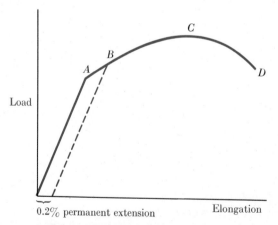

Fig. 4.5. **Load-elongation behavior of steel test specimen; *A*, elastic limit; *B*, yield stress; *C*, maximum load; *D*, fracture point.**

culated from Eq. (4.1). Plastic deformation has set in, and the specimen no longer reverts to its original length when the stress is removed. The point *B*, at which 0.2% permanent extension has taken place, is called the *yield stress*.

If stress is increased further, a point *C* is reached, called the *maximum load*. Beyond this point elongation proceeds rapidly at the neck of the specimen until it fractures at point *D*. Actually, fracture sometimes may occur at any point on the curve, but the case described is the most usual behavior.

The tensile strengths of various steels increase approximately linearly with the carbon content up to about 0.5 wt % C, as more iron is converted to iron carbide. (It is well to remember that a small weight per cent of carbon corresponds to an appreciable amount of Fe_3C. At 0.8 wt % C, one iron atom in every ten is in form of Fe_3C.) For example, at 0.2 wt % C, the tensile strength of a typical hot-rolled steel would be about 4200 kg cm^{-2}; at 0.4 wt % C, 5600 kg cm^{-2}. Addition of small amounts of manganese and phosphorus increases the strength considerably (20% or so) above these figures.

4.7   STRENGTH OF SINGLE CRYSTALS

An ordinary piece of metal has a *polycrystalline structure* like that in the photomicrograph of a steel section in Fig. 4.6. It is composed of a mass of crystallites separated by grain boundaries, at which the structures of one crystal do not fit precisely with those of adjacent crystals. Depending on the angle of misfit between the boundary planes, these grain boundaries will be regions of misfit of varying width, usually several angstroms across. The mechanical properties of a piece of metal are strongly influenced by the grain boundaries, which tend to make plastic deformation of polycrystalline metal more difficult than that in a single crystal. The grain boundaries, however, are also sources of potential weakness in a metal. It is usually easier for impurities to diffuse along grain boundaries, and as a consequence they may become regions of internal corrosion in metals. The combined effects of continual

Fig. 4.6. Grain-boundary structure of carbon-free iron—
18 ×. The solid contained oxygen as an impurity and under-
went brittle fracture along the grain boundaries. (J. R. Low,
General Electric Company, Metallurgy and Ceramics Laboratory.)

stress and chemical attack at grain boundaries can sometimes lead to catastrophic failures of metal parts. The example in Fig. 4.6 shows such an intercrystalline fracture.

Because of the much greater simplicity of the systems involved, it would seem logical to begin a quantitative study of the strength of metals by considering single crystals. We then discover at once that the big theoretical problem is not to explain why metals are so strong but why they are so weak! The permanent deformation of a perfect crystal structure should require stresses 100 to 1000 times those actually observed in tensile tests.

The argument that leads to this remarkable conclusion goes as follows: Fig. 4.7 shows a model of a shear displacement in a perfect crystal structure. As shear stress is applied to this raft of atoms, they are first displaced elastically—relieve the stress and all the atoms snap back into their original equilibrium positions. To cause a plastic deformation, we must apply enough stress to cause one layer of atoms to slip over another. We know enough about the laws of force between these metal atoms to be able to calculate, for the case of a perfect crystal, how great a stress must be applied to make one layer begin to slip over the next. The critical shear at the elastic limit cannot be more than a few degrees. The corresponding critical stress would be about $\mu/3$, where μ is the

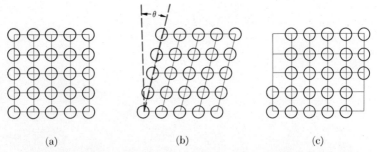

(a)   (b)   (c)

Fig. 4.7. Models of elastic and plastic deformations in a crystal. (a) Before deformation. (b) Elastic strain θ. (c) Plastic deformation.

shear modulus.[2] For aluminum, for example, the calculated $\mu = 3 \times 10^{11}$ dyne cm^{-2} and the theoretical critical shear stress would be about 10^{11} dyne cm^{-2}. When the experiment was actually tried, a single crystal of aluminum was found to be deformed permanently by a stress as low as 3×10^6 dyne cm^{-2}. This discrepancy of 30,000 between theory and experiment was one of the worst defeats ever inflicted on an atomic theory of matter. It indicated in no uncertain terms that something was fundamentally wrong in the model set up for calculation of the elastic limit. Since we used only well-established properties of metal crystals and their constituent atoms, the only escape was to admit that the pure single crystal cannot have the ideal structure on which we based our calculations.

4.8 DISLOCATIONS

What kind of defects can be lurking in the structure of a metal crystal that almost destroy its resistance to plastic deformation? They cannot be vacancies or interstitials—even a high concentration ($\sim 0.1\%$) of these point defects would have little effect on the cohesion of a metal crystal. The answer to the riddle was found in 1934—independently but almost simultaneously by three different scientists, an Englishman, G. I. Taylor, and two Hungarians, E. Orowan and M. Polanyi. They described new kinds of defects, called *dislocations*. These dislocations really govern the mechanical properties of solids. Thus, their discovery and the explication of their properties constituted one of the most important milestones in the science of materials—perhaps the single most important discovery to date in this field.

Whereas vacancies and interstitials are *point defects*, and grain boundaries are *plane defects*, a dislocation is a *line defect*. The de-

---

[2] The *shear modulus* or *rigidity* is the ratio (shear stress)/(shear strain), as measured, for example, in a torsion test. A useful relation is $\mu = Y/2(1 + \sigma)$, where σ is the *Poisson ratio*. If a specimen is stressed along the x axis, σ is the ratio of the contraction along the z axis to the extension along the x axis. See, for example, B. Chalmers, *Physical Metallurgy* (John Wiley, New York, 1959), p. 81, for an introduction to the relation between the *practical elastic constants* Y and μ, and the fundamental coefficients of elasticity theory.

fective region in the crystal lies along a definite line.   There are two
pure types of dislocations, edge dislocations and screw dislocations,
but sometimes they display a mixed type.

The *edge dislocation* is most easy to visualize.   Consider a perfect crystal structure and insert into it a half-plane of additional
atoms.   Figure 4.8a shows the result of this operation in a two-
dimensional section through a simple cubic structure, so that the
extra plane of atoms appears as an extra line.   The atoms in the
added plane AA' are shown in color.   The resulting imperfect structure now contains an *edge dislocation*.   The *dislocation line* is
formed by the cutting edge of the extra half-plane of atoms that
was inserted into the structure.   The dislocation line would be the
line perpendicular to the plane shown in Fig. 4.8a at the point
marked ⊥.   Figure 4.8b shows a three-dimensional model of an
edge dislocation.   You can easily visualize the line defect passing
through the structure at the edge of the extra plane of atoms that
has been inserted into the structure.

The other principal type of dislocation is the *screw dislocation*.
The formation of a screw dislocation can be demonstrated by a
simple model.   Take a cylinder of rubber—a solid rubber stopper
will do.   Make a cut in it from the outer surface to the axis.   Now
push the base of the stopper to create steps at the ends.   Imagine
that the rubber cylinder was filled initially with atoms arrayed on
regular lattice points.   The result of the deformation would be to
convert the parallel planes of atoms normal to the axis of the cylinder into a sort of spiral ramp.   The result of these operations is
illustrated in Fig. 4.9.   The axis of the spiral is the *dislocation line*
of the screw dislocation.   It emerges from the model shown at the
point S, and is parallel to the z axis of the figure.

If you take a piece of metal, even a single crystal, you can
twist it or bend it to various configurations, thus producing a metal
specimen with curved boundaries.   The dislocations in the crystal
structure make such curvature possible.   A mason has the same
problem on a large scale when he must build a curved structure out
of rectangular bricks.   The solution is to match $n + 1$ bricks in one
layer against n in the preceding layer.   It is simply the principle of
the arch.

A dislocation can be specified in terms of its *Burgers vector*,

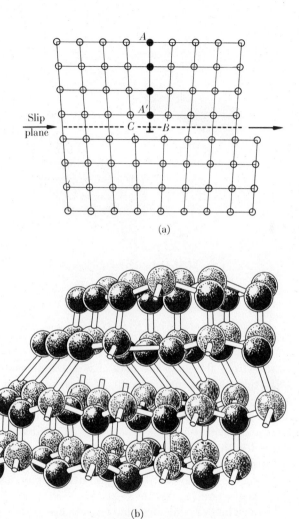

(a)

(b)

Fig. 4.8. (a) A two-dimensional section through an edge dislocation. (b) A three-dimensional ball and stick model of an edge dislocation.

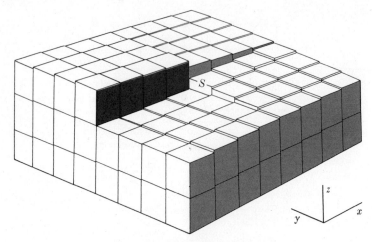

Fig. 4.9.   Model of a screw dislocation.

which is defined as follows.   In a piece of crystal with a dislocation
let us call *AB* the positive direction of the dislocation line.   At
some distance from this line, the crystal is not appreciably distorted.   Starting at an arbitrary point *M* in this "good crystal"
we make a clockwise circuit around the dislocation line by means of
any path along well-defined lattice vectors, until we come back to
N which coincides with the point *M*.   We then consider a piece of
perfect crystal with the same orientation as the original crystal.
We start from the corresponding point *M'* in the perfect crystal
and move along the exactly corresponding lattice vectors until we
come to *N'*.   If the circuit does not close and *N'* does not coincide
with *M'*, the original crystal must have contained a dislocation.
The vector from *N'* to *M'* is the *Burgers vector* of the dislocation.
It does not depend in any way on the path of the circuit around the
dislocation line or the location of the starting point.   If the Burgers
vector **b** is perpendicular to the dislocation line, the dislocation is
an edge dislocation.   If **b** is parallel to the dislocation line, the dislocation is a screw dislocation.   If **b** is not perpendicular or parallel
to the line, a *mixed dislocation* is indicated.

4.9 DISLOCATIONS AND DEFORMATION OF CRYSTALS

A dislocation can greatly facilitate deformation if it moves through a crystal by a process called *slip*. We can visualize this by considering again the two-dimensional model in Fig. 4.8a. Suppose that a shear stress acts on the dislocation from left to right. The dislocation can move from *C* to *B* relieving thereby some of the strain. If this slip continues, the dislocation finally reaches the surface of the crystal where it appears as a step. Thus, plastic deformation of the crystal can occur by this mechanism without the necessity of having one layer of atoms move across another at the expense of overcoming the strong interatomic cohesive forces between the atoms.

N. F. Mott (6) has given a neat analogy for plastic flow by way of dislocations. "We all have experience of pulling carpets over floors and know that there are two ways of doing it. One can take hold of one end and tug; or one can make a ruck in one end of the carpet and gently edge it to the other end. For a big, heavy carpet, the second way is the way to do it which involves least effort."

In a similar way, if we wish to move the top part of the crystal in Fig. 4.8a across the bottom part, we could slide one whole layer of atoms across the other, but this would be extremely difficult since it would require the simultaneous breaking of many strong bonds between metal atoms. On the other hand, we could make use of the ruck or dislocation in the crystal and cause this to glide across the crystal simply by causing atoms to glide gently in the direction of applied stress normal to the dislocation line.

The interatomic forces in a crystal offer little resistance to the gliding motion of dislocations. This is the reason why crystals of many pure metals are so soft. It is easiest to create dislocations in the closest-packed crystals. Thus they are typically very soft and ductile. Their glide planes are the planes of closest packing. On the other hand, crystals which do not have closest-packed structures, for example body-centered iron, tend to be more resistant to plastic deformation.

If we could get a crystal without dislocations it should approach its theoretical strength. Sometimes fine metallic whiskers can be grown that are virtually free of dislocations. Pure iron whiskers, for example, can have a tensile strength of up to 1.4×10^{11} dyne cm^{-2} compared to a maximum of 3×10^{10} for the strongest steel wire. The dream of metallurgists is to discover a way to produce structural metals so free of dislocations that their theoretical strengths can be achieved in practical applications.

4.10   MULTIPLICATION OF DISLOCATIONS

If you "cold-work" a piece of metal (for example, take a soft piece of copper and bend it back and forth), you can increase the concentration of dislocations in the metal by several orders of magnitude. Thus, the continued deformation of a metal in one direction does not consist simply in the sliding of dislocations already present—there is a built-in multiplication factor by which the deformation process, which occurs by way of dislocations, itself produces more dislocations. There are many different mechanisms for multiplication of dislocations, but most of them are based on the existence within the crystal of an obstacle to the glide of the dislocation.

The simplest dislocation source of this kind was described by Frank and Read in 1950. Dislocations do not usually lie entirely in one slip plane. At each end of a segment of dislocation within a given slip plane there will be a *jog* where it jumps to a neighboring slip plane. A short dislocation segment between jogs is said to be *pinned*, because if a stress is applied, the pinned dislocation cannot glide in the slip plane. The pinned dislocation is the *Frank–Read source*. The only possible motion for the pinned segment is to swell out into an arc. As stress is continued this arc expands more and more until finally it forms a complete *dislocation loop*. Then a new dislocation arc can begin to grow from the source. Under continuous moderate stress such a source can emit dislocations like an antenna broadcasting radio waves (figuratively speaking). Figure 4.10a shows in outline form the operation of a Frank–Read source and Fig. 4.10b is a remarkable electron micrograph of a dislocation source in a stainless steel that has emitted six dislocation loops.

After cold-work a crystal can contain a large number of dislocations. When such a crystal is annealed, a slow process of *polygonization* occurs. By diffusion of vacancies and interstitials, the dislocations gradually fall into a more stable configuration of grain boundaries, and stress within the crystal is relieved.

After this survey of the properties of dislocations, we can begin to answer one of the most basic questions in all metallurgy: how can the addition of a small percentage of an alloying element (carbon in steel, for example) so greatly increase the mechanical strength of a metal? The metal deforms through movements of dislocations and anything that tends to hinder such movements will increase the resistance of the metal to deformation. An impurity atom introduced into the structure of a metal will tend to situate itself in a position of minimum free energy, that is, where it must do the least work to establish itself in the structure. Generally speaking, positions in or adjacent to dislocations will therefore be sites of lower free energy for foreign atoms in a host crystal. For example, in Fig. 4.8a, a foreign atom would more readily

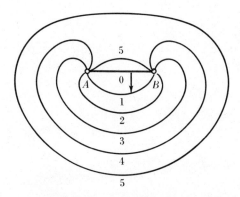

Fig. 4.10a. A Frank-Read source. When stress is applied, in the direction of the arrow, to the pinned dislocation *AB*, it emits an expanding dislocation loop. The numbers 0, 1, 2, 3, 4, 5 indicate successive positions occupied by the dislocation. At 5, having emitted a complete loop, it returns to its original situation 0.

Fig. 4.10b.   Electron micrograph (90,000 X) through thin
stainless steel foil, showing emission of dislocation loops from
a dislocation pinned at the points of arrows. [Wilsdorf (7).]

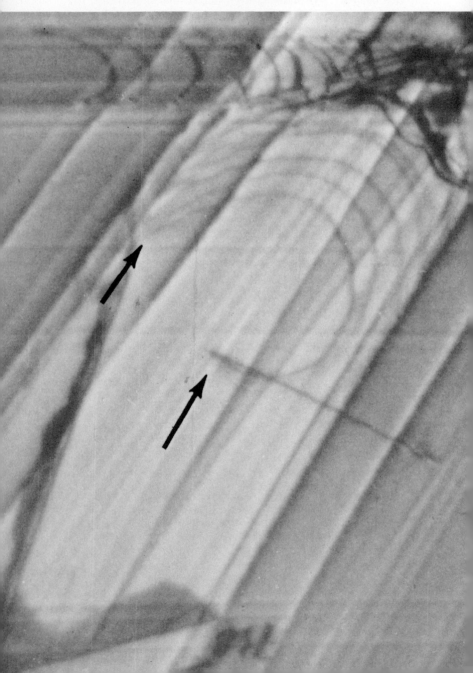

be situated at the site marked ⊥, on the dislocation, than in the normal structure. Thus foreign atoms tend to segregate at dislocations. By doing this, however, they tend to stabilize the dislocation in a definite position, locking it into place. If the dislocation were to move away and leave the foreign atoms behind, extra work would be required to establish the foreign atoms in normal structural sites. Thus, alloying elements can greatly increase the strength of metals by rendering their dislocations much less easily mobile.

4.11 DISLOCATIONS AND GROWTH OF CRYSTALS

Not only do dislocations control the mechanical properties of crystals, but they have also a profound influence on the chemical properties, how crystals grow, how they react with corrosive liquids and gases, and how they can act as catalysts of chemical reactions.

In Chapter 3 we discussed some of the problems of growing single crystals. We did not stress, however, the problem of forming the original nucleus or seed crystal from which the large crystal would grow by accretion onto its surface. Even if a seed crystal has been provided to start the growth, we still have a major problem, due to the fact that an ideally smooth and perfect crystal face provides no favorable point of attachment for additional molecules. Thus the problem of providing a nucleus would recur each time a new layer of crystal was completed. In 1949, Frank, Burton, and Cabrera (8) suggested that a crystal might escape this dilemma if it grew, not by forming perfect layers, but by adding successive units (atoms or molecules) to an evolving screw dislocation. Thus, the growth pattern would be a spiral, and the crystal would have the architectural plan not of an Egyptian pyramid but of a Babylonian ziggurat. Such a growth mechanism was illustrated in Fig. 4.9. The preferred sites for attachment of new atoms or molecules to the growing crystal would be on the colored sites at the emergent dislocation.

After this suggestion based on dislocation theory, many crystallographers began to look at growing crystals under the electron microscope, and they found numerous instances of such spiral-growth patterns, which had gone unrecognized before we had any theoretical model to explain them. A good example is shown in Fig. 4.11, which actually shows two growing spiral dislocations running into each other on the surface of a crystal. The screw-dislocation mechanism is certainly not the only way in which crystals can grow, but it evidently occurs frequently. This work emphasizes the fact that points where dislocations emerge at the surface are points of preferred chemical and physical activity on crystals.

4.12 CHEMICAL EFFECTS OF DISLOCATIONS

Dislocations are also points of preferential attack on crystal surfaces. A striking example is shown in Fig. 4.12, which shows an

Fig. 4.11. **Spiral growth pattern due to intersecting screw dislocations. (W. F. Knippenberg, Philips Research Laboratories.)**

Fig. 4.12. An emergent screw dislocation on the surface of a germanium crystal. The spiral region is 15 microns across. [Meckel and Swalin (9).]

emergent screw dislocation on the surface of a germanium crystal. The dislocation was revealed by bombarding the crystal face with argon ions. Such a picture is a sort of negative or inverse of the spiral patterns observed in crystal growth.

When a metal is etched in acid, its surface is not usually attacked smoothly and uniformly but at special points giving rise to a pattern of *etch pits*. Figure 4.13 shows the result of etching a (111) surface of a copper crystal after a particle of carborundum 60 μ in diameter had been dropped on it from a height of 2.5 cm. The pattern of etch pits reveals the dislocations that were created by the stress waves extending from the points of impact. By counting etch pits on a crystal surface we can measure directly the number of dislocations intersecting the surface of any given sample of crystal. We can also see directly how dislocations move as a result of applied stresses and how they tend to line up at boundaries between crystallites in polycrystalline specimens.

Fig. 4.13. Etch patterns along dislocations at surface of a copper crystal subjected to a light shower of hard particles. [Livingston (10).]

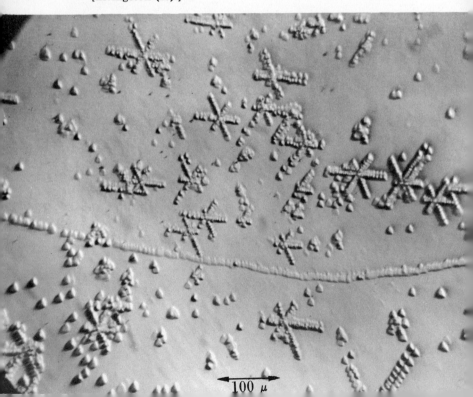

100 μ

As long ago as 1925, H. S. Taylor suggested that the catalytic activity of solid surfaces was often associated with active centers, which he visualized as isolated crystallites, corners, and edges on larger crystals. Since points where dislocations emerge are clearly active centers for removal or addition of atoms to a crystal, it was natural to ask whether they would also be sites of enhanced catalytic activity. Several careful studies have given the answer "yes" to this question. If the number of dislocations in a crystal surface is increased, its catalytic activity is often increased in proportion. In some cases, however, dislocations appear to be centers for strong adsorption of gases, but not for high catalytic activity. Perhaps the adsorbed gas is then held *too* tightly, so that the free catalyst surface cannot be renewed to take part in further reactions. Whether or not these discoveries will have any application to improving catalysts for industrial or laboratory reactions remains to be seen.

Just as crystals are most reactive at the points where dislocations stick their noses through the surface, so also in the interior of crystals, if any chemical change or phase change is to happen, it is more likely than not that it will happen at a dislocation. The precipitation of solutes along dislocation pathways in crystals leads in this way to the so-called *decoration of dislocations*. They can also be seen, however, in sufficiently thin solid films by direct transmission electron microscopy.

In brief, whenever we consider any chemical or physical change in the solid state we shall have a good probability that dislocations will act as active centers at which the changes are concentrated or localized.

4.13   FERROMAGNETISM

Much as we are tempted to do so, we cannot close a chapter on iron and steel without further mention of ferromagnetism. We are tempted to avoid this subject because of its almost mysterious nature. One of the greatest unsolved problems of solid state science is to find a theory to explain why some substances and not others display ferromagnetism.

First of all, however, what is *ferromagnetism?* When a substance is placed in a magnetic field its intensity of magnetization M is proportional to the strength of the field H

$$M = \chi H$$

The proportionality factor χ is called the *magnetic susceptibility* of the substance. For most substances χ is either very small and negative (diamagnetism) or small and positive (paramagnetism). There are some solids for which χ is much larger—about 10^4 times its value for a typical paramagnetic substance. These are called *ferromagnets* because iron is the prototype of such materials.

It is easy enough to see in a qualitative way how such a large magnetization can arise. The intensity of magnetization M is the magnetic moment per unit volume. Magnetic moment is a vector quantity. Think of it as an arrow directed from the north to the south pole of a magnet, with a length equal to the strength of the magnetic pole. (A unit magnetic pole is defined as one that exerts a force of one dyne on a similar pole a distance one centimeter away in a vacuum.) In a cubic centimeter of material we can have many atomic magnetic dipoles. If we add these all vectorially, the resultant is M, the intensity of magnetization.

The way to get a *very large M* is therefore clear—a large number of small magnets must line up in the field to give a large resultant moment. Furthermore, in a ferromagnet, the little magnets remain lined up even when the external field is removed. What keeps them lined up?

Strangely enough, this problem is closely related to the wave mechanical theory of the chemical bond. You will recall that Heitler and London were able to give an explanation of the covalent bond between two hydrogen atoms based on a model in which a pair of electrons with antiparallel spins were shared between the two hydrogen nuclei (protons). The same kind of theory when applied to the electrons in a ferromagnetic substance indicated that the stable state should be one in which pairs of electrons in neighboring atoms have *parallel spins*.

Weiss devised a theory according to which a ferromagnet was composed of *domains*, within each of which the spins were aligned so as to give large net magnetic moments. When a system like this is placed between the poles of a magnet and the field increased, its magnetization can increase by two different mechanisms—(1) The walls of the domains can be displaced so as to increase the volumes of those lined up in the field. (2) The resultant magnets within domains can rotate so as to align more nearly with the field. Experiments showed that, in weaker fields, magnetization was due primarily to displacement of domain boundaries, but, in stronger fields, rotation of moments within individual domains occurred.

Fig. 4.14. Magnetization processes according to domain model and typical magnetization curve for iron. [After C. Kittel (11).]

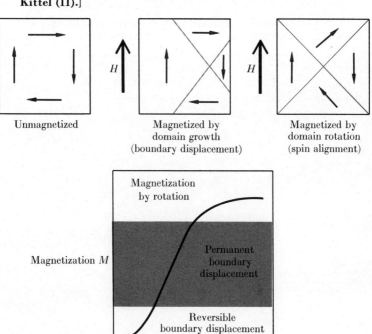

Unmagnetized

Magnetized by domain growth (boundary displacement)

Magnetized by domain rotation (spin alignment)

Magnetization by rotation

Permanent boundary displacement

Magnetization M

Reversible boundary displacement

Magnetic field strength H

The magnetization curve of Fig. 4.14 thus includes sections caused by each of these two mechanisms.

A method that makes the domains visible by direct microscopic examination was devised by Bitter (12). A very finely divided iron powder or colloidal suspension is spread over the polished surface of the crystals, and the powder grains line up in the magnetic fields of the individual domains. One of Bitter's original domain patterns obtained in this way is shown in Fig. 4.15.

A good question is, Why does the magnetic system break up into domains? The answer is as follows. The exchange interaction that causes spins to be parallel on neighboring atoms is a short-range interaction, extending over at most next nearest neighbors. As in the case of the H_2 molecule it is an electrostatic interaction that is connected indirectly with the spins because of the

Fig. 4.15. **Magnetic-domain patterns on surface of an individual crystal of iron.**

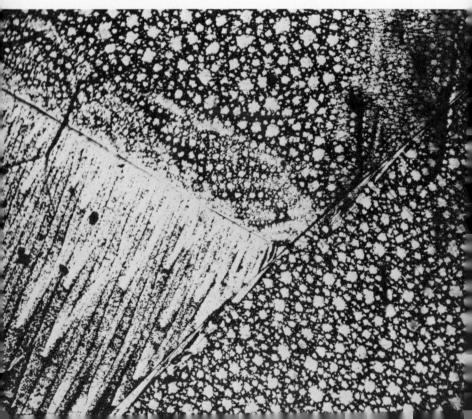

form of the wave functions allowed for the electrons. There is in addition, however, a much smaller direct magnetic interaction, which increases the energy of the system when the spins are parallel. This interaction is comparatively a long-range one (falling off as about the cube of the distance between atoms). Ultimately, therefore, a point will be reached at which the system can lower its energy by reversing the spins beyond a certain distance from a given spin. Hence, the magnetic system breaks up into a pattern of domains.

Does this story have any importance for the student of chemistry? Actually, it has a great deal. First, ferromagnetism provides a way of studying electronic interactions that are in many ways similar to those of chemical bonding; thus it may provide clues to long-range effects within polymer molecules or at distances from solid surfaces. Second, the chemical theory of ferromagnetism is still mysterious: we do not know what kinds of crystals can show this and related phenomena, and why. The theory of the transitions between magnetized and unmagnetized states provides a useful analog of other phase transitions, such as melting or superconductivity. Finally, remanent magnetism in rocks and minerals provides a record of past history of the earth and is hence of great geochemical interest. All these fields and a few more depend on a better understanding of the ancient lodestone.

REFERENCES

(1) C. S. Smith, *A History of Metallography* (Chicago: University of Chicago Press, 1960). This fascinating book gives details about many historic problems of steel making.

(2) L. Pauling, *The Nature of the Chemical Bond*, 3rd ed. (Ithaca, N.Y.: Cornell University Press, 1960), p. 414.

(3) J. B. Austin, *Metals Handbook* (Cleveland: American Society for Metals, 1948), p. 1181.

(4) C. M. Wayman, *Introduction to the Crystallography of Martensitic Transformations* (New York: Macmillan, 1964).

(5) A. H. Cottrell, *The Mechanical Properties of Matter* (New York: Wiley, 1964).

(6) N. F. Mott, *Atomic Structure and the Strength of Metals* (New York: Pergamon Press, 1956).

(7) H. G. F. Wilsdorf, "On the Multiplication of Dislocations in Thin Foils," in *Structure and Properties of Thin Films* (New York: Wiley, 1959).

(8) F. C. Frank, *Discussions Faraday Soc.* **5**, 48 (1949).

(9) B. B. Meckel and R. A. Swalin, *J. Appl. Phys.* **30**, 89 (1959).

(10) J. D. Livingston, "Positive and Negative Dislocations in Copper," in *Direct Observations of Imperfections in Crystals*, J. B. Newkirk and J. H. Wernick, ed. (New York: Interscience, 1962).

(11) C. Kittel, *Introduction to Solid State Physics*, 3rd ed. (New York: Wiley, 1966).

(12) F. Bitter, *Magnets, The Education of a Physicist* (New York: Doubleday Anchor Books, 1959). Interesting material on magnetism by a pioneer in the field.

V

Nickel Oxide

Nickel oxide is a remarkable solid. At first it looks dark gray and unexciting, but later it may display an emerald green and reveal unexpected depths and mysteries. At one time the grand edifice of the band theory of solids threatened to topple into disorder, simply because of the anomalous situation of NiO. According to band theory, NiO should have the high electrical conductivity of a metal, since the $3d$ band of the Ni^{2+} ions, which can hold 10 electrons, would be only partly filled. In fact, however, pure NiO is a good insulator.

5.1 CRYSTAL STRUCTURE

For many years the crystal structure of NiO was listed as the NaCl type. In 1943, Rooksby discovered that at ordinary temperatures the structure of NiO was slightly distorted from the ideal cubic NaCl structure, which was shown in Fig. 1.8. If we look at this structure along a 3-fold axis, that is, a [111] direction, we can consider it to be made up of alternate planes of Cl^- ions and Na^+ ions in closely packed layers. To be sure, because of the difference in their ionic sizes, both Cl^- and Na^+ layers cannot be closest packed, but the arrangement within the layers is still that of closest packing, six ions hexagonally arranged around each given central ion. Viewed in this way, the structure might conveniently be based on a rhombohedral unit cell with $\alpha = 60°$ and $a = a_0/2^{1/2}$, where a_0 is the cubic cell length. The ratio of ionic sizes in NaCl is $r(Na^+)/r(Cl^-) = 0.53$. In NiO, however, the ratio is somewhat smaller, $r(Ni^{2+})/r(O^{2-}) = 0.49$. Evidently, the NiO structure can gain stability by squeezing slightly inward along the 3-fold axis. The resultant rhombohedral angle becomes $\alpha = 60°4.2'$ at 18°. If the crystal is chilled in liquid nitrogen to $-183°C$, the distortion increases to $\alpha = 60°12'$. If the crystal is warmed above room temperature, the distortion decreases smoothly, and above 250°C the crystal has the NaCl structure with $\alpha = 60°$ exactly.

5.2 MAGNETIC STRUCTURE OF NICKEL OXIDE

The nickel ion has the configuration $3d^8$ and electrons can fill the five $3d$ orbitals as follows:

Thus, there are two electrons with unpaired spins and one might expect NiO to be a paramagnetic substance, following the Curie law of variation of magnetic susceptibility χ with T: $\chi = N\mu^2/3kT$, where N is the number per unit volume of elementary magnets each having a moment μ. According to this law, the susceptibility decreases with temperature because the thermal vibrations of the ions tend to destroy the orientation of the magnets by the external field.

The experimental susceptibility χ versus temperature T curve

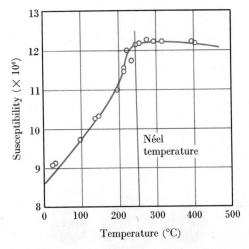

Fig. 5.1.   Magnetic susceptibility of NiO as function of temperature.

is shown in Fig. 5.1.   The susceptibility actually increases with temperature up to about 250°C and only above this temperature does it begin to decrease in accord with the paramagnetic model. This behavior is typical of an *antiferromagnetic* substance, and the temperature 250°C at which antiferromagnetism becomes paramagnetism is called the *Néel temperature*.   It corresponds in this case to the transformation of NiO from a rhombohedral to a cubic structure.

In an antiferromagnet the spins are lined up in a regular array, but they are not all pointed in the same direction as they are in a ferromagnet. Instead a layer of spins in one direction may be followed by a layer in the opposite direction, and so on.   The spins are thus ordered but they do not reinforce one another to give a high overall magnetic moment. An experimental method exists for the determination of such an ordered spin structure, namely, analysis of neutron diffraction by the crystal. Neutrons have no charge but they do have a spin and hence a beam of neutrons is like a beam of little magnets.   Whereas scattering of x rays or elec-

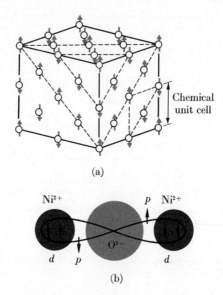

(a)

(b)

Fig. 5.2. (a) **Magnetic superstructure of NiO. Only the Ni^{2+}
ions are shown, with orientations of their net spins indicated
by arrows. (b) Superexchange through p electrons of oxygen
couples spins of d electrons of Ni.**

trons in a crystal structure is controlled by electrostatic forces,
scattering of a beam of neutrons is sensitive mainly to magnetic
forces. When examined by neutron diffraction, NiO was shown to
have a magnetic unit cell that is just twice the length of the crystallographic unit cell. The spins within any given 111 close-
packed layer point in the opposite direction to those in adjacent
layers. This magnetic structure is shown in Fig. 5.2a. Only the
Ni^{2+} ions are shown; the O^{2-} ions, which do not contribute directly
to the magnetic properties, lie on a second fcc lattice displaced half
a unit cell distance from the lattice occupied by the Ni^{2+} ions.
Thus, there is a layer of O^{2-} ions between every two layers of Ni^{2+}
ions.

How do the electrons in one layer of Ni^{2+} interact with the
spins in the next layer of Ni^{2+} when they are separated by a layer of

O^{2-} ions? An interesting explanation of this long-range interaction has been given. It is called *superexchange*. The d electrons of an Ni^{2+} ion in one layer are coupled magnetically with p electrons of an O^{2-} ion, which in turn interact with the d electrons of a Ni^{2+} in the next layer. This superexchange process is shown schematically in Fig. 5.2b.

5.3 ELECTRONIC STRUCTURE OF NICKEL OXIDE

According to the classical band theory of solids, as Ni^{2+} ions are brought together in a regular array, their $3d$ orbitals should overlap to form a $3d$ band in the solid state, capable of holding 10 electrons. Since only 8 electrons are available, this band can be only partly filled. Hence, NiO should be a conductor of electricity like a metal. Since in fact the material is an excellent insulator when pure, the band theory was faced here with a disconcerting Gegenbeispiel.

At first the ferromagnetic structure just described seemed to provide a facile way out of the difficulty. An electron could not move from one nickel site to the next without carrying along its spin, and hence it would be prevented from moving in NiO by the existence of the antiferromagnetic superstructure. Effectively, the $3d$ band would be split into two subbands each of which would hold electrons of one spin. A nice theory—but it would predict that above the Néel temperature, where antiferromagnetism is destroyed, NiO should become a much better conductor. No such improvement in conductivity was observed and hence this way out of the difficulty was blocked.

The next suggestion was that we should not consider the $3d$ levels of Ni^{2+} as forming a single $3d$ band. We should consider the effect on the $3d$ electrons of the electrostatic field of the surrounding O^{2-} ions, the so-called *crystal field* or *ligand field*. Each Ni^{2+} is surrounded octahedrally by six O^{2-} so that the problem was how a field with octahedral symmetry might split the $3d$ levels. The answer was well known. The field splits the levels into a lower set of three (d_{xy}, d_{yz}, d_{xz}) and an upper set of two (d_{z^2}, $d_{x^2-y^2}$). If we fill the lower three orbitals completely with six electrons, we still have two left over and these cannot possibly fill the upper set also. Hence, crystal-field splitting cannot blunt the horns of our dilemma. Even when split by the crystal field, energy bands should still exist, and the upper one would be only partly filled so that NiO should still be a conductor on this model.

5.4 ESCAPE FROM NiO DILEMMA—MOTT THEORY

In a group of papers beginning in 1949, N. F. Mott provided the most reasonable explanation of the properties of NiO and in so doing a startling new insight into the theory of such solid states. Let us consider, in accord with Mott, a model consisting of a simple cubic lattice on each point of which is placed an atom with a single valence electron, for instance, a hydrogen atom or a lithium atom. According to band theory, there will be some overlap of electronic wave functions so that the correct wave function for the array will be a Bloch function like that described in Section 2.7,

$$u_{\mathbf{k}}(r)e^{i\mathbf{k}r}$$

These will give a band of allowed energy levels, which in this case would be only half filled so that the substance would behave as a metallic conductor. Suppose, however, we allow the distance between atoms on our lattice to become larger and larger. According to the band model, the overlap of electron wave functions will become less and less, and the width of the band will become narrower and narrower, but the substance will still remain a metallic conductor. The less the overlap, the narrower the band, and the narrower the band, the larger the effective mass m^* of the electron in the band. At large interatomic distances we should thus expect to have terribly sluggish electrons but they would still be able to move freely throughout the solid even at the limit of absolute zero. In other words, there would be no energy of activation required to make the electrons mobile. (This is the essential difference between a metal and a semiconductor. As $T \to 0$ the conductivity of a semiconductor must also $\to 0$ since it depends on an $\exp(-\epsilon/kT)$ factor.)

When Mott first examined this situation, his physical intuition told him that it must be contrary to fact. Only later did he devise a mathematical discussion to support his original insight. We shall summarize his final analysis (1) of the problem.

When the distance R between atoms on the lattice becomes large, the process of moving a charge from one atom to another is simply that of taking an electron from one,

$$M \rightarrow M^+ + e^-$$

and putting it on its neighbor,

$$M + e^- \rightarrow M^-$$

The first reaction requires an energy I, the ionization potential, and the second gives back an energy A, the electron affinity. Thus ΔE of the electron transfer reaction in the limit of large R must become

$$\Delta E = I - A$$

For the usual atoms of interest this quantity is quite markedly positive; that is, energy must be provided from some source in order to cause the transfer of an electron. In the solid, however, the ΔE would not be so great as in the gas and it might be worthwhile to pay the price if the electron removed from one site could then move freely through the solid. Yet it is most unlikely that the electron so produced would be free to move. The site from which the electron was removed would have an effective positive charge, and the electron would be attracted toward this charge. The attractive potential would have the form,

$$U = \frac{-e^2}{r}$$

Thus the electron would be trapped by the positive hole it left behind—like a small dog that digs a hole, falls into it and cannot get out.

As more electrons are removed from parent atoms, a new factor enters the situation. These electrons begin to create a screen of negative charge around the positive centers, so that the attraction of a positive hole for any given electron is much reduced. The potential in this case takes the form,[1]

$$U = \left(\frac{-e^2}{r}\right) \exp\,(-\lambda r) \tag{5.1}$$

where λ is called the *screening constant*. The reciprocal of $\lambda(\lambda^{-1})$ is called the *screening radius*. It has the following physical significance: the screened positive charge cannot be seen (felt, sensed, or attracted, if you prefer) by the electron when it is at a distance of more than three or four times λ^{-1} from the electron. The detailed theory shows that

$$\lambda^2 = \frac{16\pi^2 e^2 m N^{1/3}}{h^2} \tag{5.2}$$

where N is the density of ionized electrons (the number of electrons per unit volume). When a Coulombic field binds an electron, the ground state has a radius equal to the Bohr radius of the hydrogen atom,

$$a_0 = \frac{h^2}{4\pi^2 m e^2}$$

If the screening radius λ^{-1} is less than a_0, the electron cannot be bound. The condition for binding is therefore

$$\lambda^{-1} > a_0$$

Thus the density at which binding is no longer possible is given by

$$N^{-1/3} > 4a_0 \tag{5.3}$$

Since N is the number of electrons per cubic centimeter, $N^{-1/3}$ can be interpreted as the average distance in centimeters between electrons. Thus when the spacing between atoms becomes greater than about 4 atomic units, the ionized state can no longer be achieved and the substance should become an insulator at absolute zero. As the atoms are brought together the transition from insulator to metal should be quite sharp, somewhere about $R \lesssim 4a_0$.

---

[1] This is the same potential found in the Debye-Hückel theory of dilute strong electrolytes for a central ion surrounded by an "ionic atmosphere."

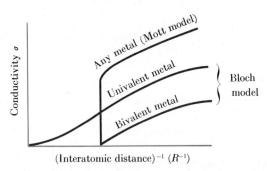

Fig. 5.3. Electrical conductivity as function of interatomic distance as predicted by different model theories of the solid state.

Mott's conclusions are summarized in Fig. 5.3, which shows how the conductivity, which is proportional to the number of free electrons, should vary with the interatomic distance. Actually, for clarity, σ is plotted versus R^{-1} so that the origin at $R^{-1} = 0$ represents infinite separation of the atoms. The contrast between the Mott theory and the earlier band theory of Wilson and Bloch is clear-cut. The Mott theory differs from older models of the solid state in predicting a rather sharp transition from insulator to metal as the interatomic distance decreases.

Let us recall that the Bloch model predicted for a bivalent metal an overlap of a filled band with an empty band, leading to metallic properties. At large interatomic distances this overlap would decrease and ultimately the metal would lose its conductivity. The Mott picture is a radically different view of the solid state and has some most interesting predictions. For example, if we compress an insulator with unfilled orbitals, we may finally reach a point at which the interatomic distance becomes small enough to cause a sharp transition to the metallic state. Similarly, if we raise the temperature of a semiconductor high enough, it is possible that the number of electrons will become great enough so that the screening overcomes the trapping effect and again there will be a transition from a semiconductor to a metal.

Actually, in the case of NiO it has not yet been possible to achieve either pressures or temperatures high enough to reach a transition to a metallic state. High-pressure measurements have been taken up to about 500 kilobars[2] and the resistance has fallen by a factor of about 3, but it would apparently be necessary to go to pressures of tens of megabars to have a chance of finding the metallic transition. In the cases of silicon and germanium, however, Drickamer (2) found a transition from semiconducting to metallic state at high pressures. The energy gap went to zero and the crystal structure changed from diamond to white-tin type. Also in the cases of zinc sulfide, zinc selenide and zinc telluride, the transitions from semiconducting to metallic state have been observed. These cases are not exact illustrations of the Mott theory, however, since they do not involve electronic structures for which unfilled bands would be predicted. They can most conveniently be explained by a decrease in the band gap with increasing overlap until finally the gap goes to zero and the conduction band merges with the valence band. Nevertheless, the results are of great interest in showing how the properties of solids may change dramatically at high pressures. These results recall a provocative paper published by Wigner and Huntington in 1935 (3) concerning the possibility of a metallic form of hydrogen. The model used in this paper was quite similar to that of Mott, in that atomic hydrogen in principle might have a band structure that is only half filled. In fact, it represents a good example of the idealized Mott metal. Wigner speculated that at the pressures existing in some stars hydrogen should be in a metallic state. Once again the temperatures and pressures necessary are outside the range of present earthly apparatus.

Probably one of the best examples of a Mott transition in an oxide was observed in vandium monoxide (VO) by F. J. Morin (4). His data are shown in Fig. 5.4. At a temperature of 120–125°K, VO displays an abrupt drop in resistance by a factor of over 10^5. Even more significantly, below the transition temperature its conductivity increases steeply with rise in temperature, as expected for a semiconductor, but above the transition temperature its

---

[2] One atmosphere = 1.01325 bar.

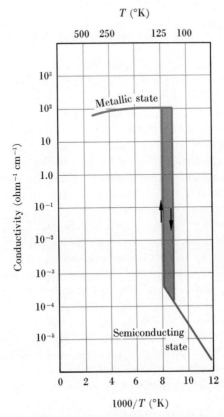

Fig. 5.4. Conductivity of vanadium monoxide as function of temperature. (The transition temperature varies somewhat with preparation of sample and depending on whether measurements are made on warming or on cooling.)

conductivity decreases slowly with the temperature as expected of a typical metal. Since the 3*d* band of V in VO would have spaces for ten electrons and only three electrons are provided by the V^{2+} ion, the case is quite similar to that of NiO. Also both NiO and VO have the rock salt structure.

5.5 NONSTOICHIOMETRY

Depending on how it is made, NiO may range in color from pale apple green to jet black. For example, if you lightly oxidize a strip of pure Ni at about 800°C, it becomes covered by a film of pale green NiO. This film is easily soluble in dilute acid, is transparent, and is a good insulator. On the other hand, if you completely oxidize a Ni strip at about 1200°C, you get a solid black piece of NiO, which can be boiled for days in dilute or concentrated acid without any detectable solubility. This material also has an appreciable conductivity with a temperature coefficient following the equation typical of a semiconductor, $\sigma = \sigma_0 \exp(-\epsilon/kT)$.

The essential difference between green and black NiO is that the green crystal has almost exactly the stoichiometric composition of one Ni to one O atom, corresponding to the formula $Ni_{1.00}O_{1.00}$. The black material, however, has an excess of O or more precisely a deficiency of Ni with a formula averaging $Ni_{0.98}O_{1.00}$. Black NiO therefore violates the law of definite proportions. It belongs to the class of *nonstoichiometric compounds*.

Such compounds are often called *berthollides* and those following strictly the law of definite proportions are called *daltonides*. Gaseous compounds are always daltonides, but in the solid state the law of definite proportions is as likely to be breached as observed.

The history of these compounds and names harks back to one of the most famous controversies in the history of chemistry. In 1803, Claude Louis Berthollet, then the leader of French chemistry, published a book, *Essai de Statique Chimique*, in which he argued most vehemently that he could change the final compositions of chemical compounds by changing the proportions of reactants in the mixture from which they were synthesized. An important example was zinc oxide, which he found to contain more zinc proportionately as he increased the ratio of zinc to oxygen in the reaction mixture. At that time probably the best chemical analyst in Europe was Joseph Louis Proust. He rechecked all of Berthollet's experiments, repeated the analyses, and showed pretty conclusively that ZnO and other compounds cited by Berthollet had fixed compositions, no matter how they were synthesized. The victory of Proust firmly established the law of definite proportions, so that John Dalton in 1808 was able to rely on this foundation when he formulated his atomic theory.

The ironic postscript to this history is that, although Berthollet lost the controversy and his analyses were wrong, nevertheless he turned out to be correct in his belief that the law of definite proportions, so far as solid substances are concerned, is far from inviolable. Zinc oxide can be made so as to contain more atoms of Zn than of O, not nearly so many more as Berthollet thought, but up to a composition of $Zn_{1.00033}O_{1.00}$, that is, 0.033 atom % excess over stoichiometric. This excess Zn fits into interstitial sites in the ZnO crystal structure and causes the normally white crystals to become a bright orange-red. As shown in Fig. 5.5a the excess "interstitial Zn," Zn_i, in ZnO can act as a source of electrons,

$$Zn_i \rightarrow Zn_i^+ + e^-$$

If an interstitial Zn is ionized and its electron enters the conduction band, the crystal becomes an n-type semiconductor. The simple band model for such a substance resembles that for silicon with n-type impurities, with donor levels (in this case excess Zn_i) lying just under the conduction band. In Fig. 5.5a, ZnO is depicted as an ionic structure $Zn^{2+}O^{2-}$, but various estimates suggest that there is considerable covalent binding in ZnO, and the effective charge on the Zn atoms may be nearer $+1$ than $+2$ as a result of electron sharing between atoms. The band gap in ZnO is about 3.0 eV at 25°C, but it decreases with increasing temperature. This decrease has a curious consequence: if you heat ZnO it turns from white to yellow, but as it cools it becomes white again. At elevated temperatures the band gap is decreased enough to give rise to an optical absorption band in the violet region, causing the crystals to appear yellow.

Like ZnO, NiO can depart from ideal stoichiometry, except that now there is an excess of oxygen. The oxygen atom is too large to permit any considerable concentration of interstitial O atoms in the structure; consequently, solution of excess O in NiO creates vacancies in the normally occupied Ni sites. The result is

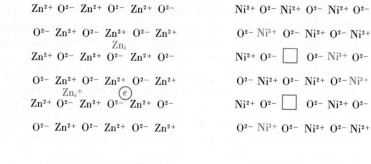

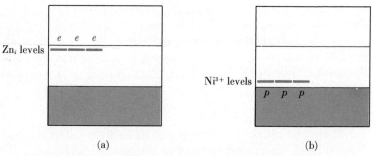

Fig. 5.5. **Nonstoichiometric crystals.** (a) **Excess interstitial Zn in ZnO makes it an *n*-type semiconductor.** (b) **Excess O in NiO leads to cation vacancies and makes it a *p*-type semiconductor.**

shown in Fig. 5.5b. In order to preserve overall electrical neutrality in the crystal, two Ni^{2+} ions must be converted to Ni^{3+} for every vacant Ni^{2+} site. The Ni^{3+} ions introduced into the crystal in this way can be considered to be positive centers capable of jumping from one Ni^{2+} site to another. Notice that the ions themselves do not move. When an electron hops from a Ni^{2+} to a Ni^{3+} site it is as if a positive hole moves through the Ni^{2+} sites. Thus NiO with excess oxygen is a *p*-type semiconductor. We can write the ionization of a positive hole as

$$Ni^{3+} \rightarrow Ni^{2+} + p \quad \text{or} \quad Ni^{2+} - e^- \rightarrow Ni^{3+}$$

We represent this process in Fig. 5.5b as the acceptance of an electron by an acceptor site such as Ni^{3+} introduced into the crystal by the excess oxygen. The overall solution of excess oxygen can be written

$$2Ni^{2+} + \tfrac{1}{2}O_2 \rightarrow O^{2-} + V_c + 2Ni^{3+}$$

where V_c denotes a vacancy at a cation site in the structure. This equation shows that for each extra O^{2-} ion in the crystal there must be one vacant cation site and two Ni^{3+} ions. The equilibrium constant of the reaction becomes

$$K = \frac{[Ni^{3+}]^2[V_c][O^{2-}]}{P_{O_2}^{1/2}}$$

The activity of O^{2-} ion is effectively constant since it represents the major component of the crystal. Also it is evident that $[V_c] = [Ni^{3+}]$. Therefore,

$$[V_c] = [Ni^{3+}] = K^{1/3}P_{O_2}^{1/6} \qquad (5.4)$$

If the conductivity σ is proportional to the number of positive holes $[Ni^{3+}]$ and these are not bound to vacancies, σ should vary as $P_{O_2}^{1/6}$. Actually, the measured σ varies approximately as $P_{O_2}^{1/5}$. This imperfect agreement with theory has been ascribed to incomplete dissociation of the Ni^{3+} from the vacancies.

The theory of the conductivity of NiO containing excess oxygen still presents some problems. The conductivity depends on temperature in accord with an Arrhenius type expression as used for a semiconductor, $\sigma = \sigma_o \exp(-\epsilon/kT)$, with activation energy[3] $\epsilon \approx 2.5$ eV. There are two ways of explaining this activation energy. If we apply a band model to NiO with excess oxygen we find the picture in Fig. 5.5b. The Ni^{3+} sites act as impurity levels above the filled band and the excitation of an electron to these sites leaves mobile holes in the band. This model would treat NiO as similar to a p-type semiconductor such as silicon doped with boron (p. 84). In view of the serious difficulties of the band model for pure NiO, which were discussed at the beginning of the chapter, this picture seems dubious for nonstoichiometric NiO also.

---

[3] The activation energy varies with oxygen pressure and with impurities in the crystal but the value cited is typical of pure single crystals in air.

There is an experimential way to check the band model. If
the positive holes exist in an otherwise filled band, it should be possible to detect them and to measure their mobility by means of the
Hall effect. Hall-effect measurements of NiO have been made but
they indicate an extremely low mobility for the positive holes. The
most simple explanation seems to be that the charge is localized on
the Ni^{3+} ion until it receives enough thermal energy to jump to a
neighboring site. That is to say, the activation energy is not provided merely to introduce into a valence band a positive hole,
which then is highly mobile throughout the crystal when an electric field is applied. In NiO, activation energy apparently must be
provided also for each jump of a positive hole from one site to the
next. This type of conduction process has caused NiO to be called
a *hopping semiconductor* (5).

5.6 A THERMOELECTRIC EFFECT

Temperature gradients in materials with mobile charge carriers can lead to gradients in electric potential, and vice versa.
Effects of this kind are called *thermoelectric effects*. They yield
valuable information about the current carriers in semiconductors.
They are also of practical importance in devices such as thermo-
couples for measuring temperature and in thermoelectric cooling
equipment. Some engineers believe that thermoelectric cooling
may replace conventional refrigerators in applications where con-
siderations of weight and space are decisive.

A simple thermoelectric effect is the Seebeck effect illustrated
in Fig. 5.6. A sample of the solid to be studied is mounted so that
one end B is in contact with a colder reservoir at temperature T
while the other end A is in contact with a warmer reservoir at $T +
\Delta T$. If a potentiometer is connected across the two terminals, at
equilibrium there is a difference in electrical potential $\Delta\phi$ between
A and B, such that

$$\Delta\phi = \phi_A - \phi_B = -\alpha(T_A - T_B) \qquad (5.5)$$

where α is called the *Seebeck coefficient*. If $\Delta\phi$ is measured in volts,
the units of α are volts per degree.

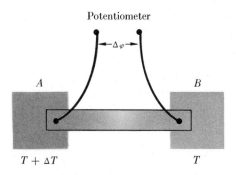

Fig. 5.6. The Seebeck effect: A temperature gradient in a conductor causes an electric-potential gradient.

The cause of the potential difference can be understood as follows. The charge carriers in the hot region, predominantly electrons or positive holes as the case may be, will have a higher kinetic energy (and hence higher velocity) than those in the cold region. Thus, when the temperature gradient is established, more carriers will flow from hot to cold than vice versa, until a potential difference is set up sufficient to block further flow of charge. Thus, if the majority charge carriers are positive, the cold region will become positively charged; if they are negative, the cold region will become negatively charged.

Another way to look at this situation is to consider the Fermi (electrochemical) potential $\bar{\mu}$, where

$$\bar{\mu} = \mu + ze\phi \qquad (5.6)$$

Here μ is the chemical potential and ze is the charge. When one side is raised in temperature the Fermi potential of its carriers will rise and they will flow over to the other side, until equality of Fermi potentials is reestablished:

$$\mu_A + ze\phi_A = \mu_B + ze\phi_B$$

or

$$ze(\phi_A - \phi_B) = \mu_B - \mu_A$$

The potentiometer therefore measures the difference in electric potential between the terminals A and B.

The measurement of the sign of the Seebeck coefficient thus tells us immediately whether the predominant charge carriers are positive or negative. For NiO, the measured α is positive, indicating that conduction is due mainly to positive holes.

The theory of the Seebeck coefficient relates it also to the concentration N_D of donor or acceptor centers in a semiconductor:

$$\alpha = \frac{k}{e} (\ln \frac{N_0}{N_D} + a) \tag{5.7}$$

Here N_0 is the number of metal-ion sites and a is a constant. Notice the remarkable fact that the fewer the number N_D of donors or acceptors, the larger is α. Thus α becomes quite large and easily measurable in crystals like NiO even when they contain only a small concentration of positive holes. Therefore, semiconductors of this type may be especially useful in devices for thermoelectric cooling.

5.7   NICKEL OXIDE DOPED WITH LITHIUM

If NiO can be made into a better conductor by introducing Ni^{3+} ions into the structure, can we find an easier way to do this than by heating the crystal in oxygen? In 1948 Verwey discovered that NiO can dissolve large amounts of Li_2O. The crystal radius of Ni^{2+} is 0.69 Å and that of Li^+ is 0.60 Å, so that Li^+ can easily displace Ni^{2+} without appreciable distortion of the structure. For every Li^+ that enters the structure, one Ni^{2+} is oxidized to Ni^{3+} in order to maintain electrical neutrality.

The situation that results on doping NiO with lithium is shown in Fig. 5.7a. Note that we can obtain a high concentration of Ni^{3+} in the structure without any extra vacancies at Ni^{2+} sites. The presence of Li^+ in the structure stabilizes the presence of an equivalent number of Ni^{3+} ions which would otherwise have the normal oxidation state of Ni^{2+}. This process is called *valence induction*. NiO doped with lithium becomes black in color and an excellent conductor of electricity. Figure 5.7b shows how the resistivity of

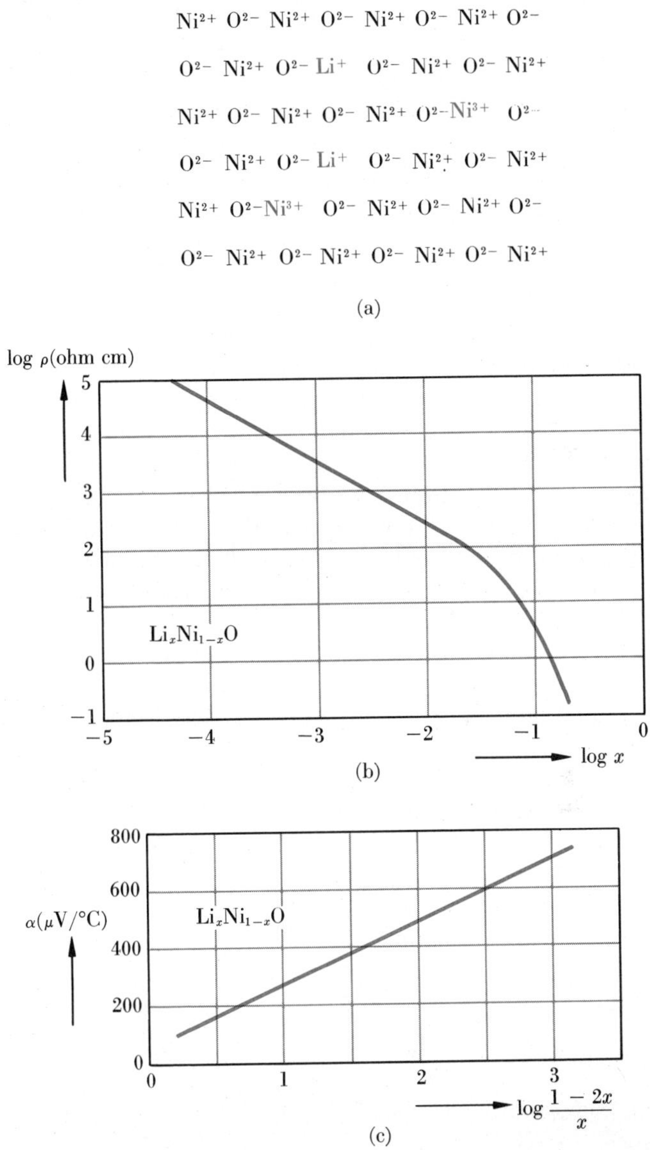

Ni2+ O2− Ni2+ O2− Ni2+ O2− Ni2+ O2−
O2− Ni2+ O2− Li+ O2− Ni2+ O2− Ni2+
Ni2+ O2− Ni2+ O2− Ni2+ O2− Ni3+ O2−
O2− Ni2+ O2− Li+ O2− Ni2+ O2− Ni2+
Ni2+ O2− Ni3+ O2− Ni2+ O2− Ni2+ O2−
O2− Ni2+ O2− Ni2+ O2− Ni2+ O2− Ni2+
(a)
log ρ(ohm cm)
5
4
3
2
1
0
−1
−5
−4
−3
−2
−1
0
LixNi1−xO
log x
(b)
800
600
400
200
0
α(μV/°C)
LixNi1−xO
0
1
2
3
log (1 − 2x)/x
(c)

Fig. 5.7. Effects of doping NiO with Li. (a) Doping of NiO with Li introduces positive holes into structure as Ni^{3+} ions. (b) Resistivity of $Li_xNi_{1-x}O$ as a function of Li concentration. (c) Seebeck effect of $Li_xNi_{1-x}O$ as a function of the Li concentration. (Note that positive abscissa corresponds to decrease in x in this plot.)

NiO decreases as the lithium content increases and Fig. 5.7c shows the variation of Seebeck coefficient with added lithium.

We should note carefully that despite its high conductivity the crystal $Li_xNi_{1-x}O$ still behaves as a semiconductor and not as a metal. Its resistivity still decreases with increasing temperature. For example, the resistivity of $Li_{0.05}Ni_{0.95}O$ over most of the range up to 500°K follows a regular exponential-type temperature dependence with an activation energy of 0.15 eV. What is the origin of this activation energy? Part of it arises from the fact that before positive holes on Ni^{3+} can move, they must get away from the Li^+ ions. At absolute zero, for example, the most stable state would always place a Ni^{3+} adjacent to a Li^+, since in this way the electrostatic energy would be minimized. Even when the positive Ni^{3+} lets go the hand of its negative mother,[4] however, it is still not free to travel in the crystal. We now have the hopping problem again. The extra positive charge is trapped on the Ni^{3+} owing to the fact that it polarizes the surrounding structure, digging itself a sort of electrical hole to which energy must be supplied to set it free. Thus, its motion through a crystal is an activated hopping from one site to another. In view of the considerable increase in positive holes caused by doping with lithium it is likely that the screening of the holes from the hole centers is quite effective. My guess would be that once the hole gets away from the Li^+ it is fairly free to move through the doped crystal.

5.8 OXIDATION OF NICKEL

The burning of a magnesium flare, the tarnishing of a new penny, the rusting of iron—these familiar reactions remind us that with a few noble exceptions, like gold or platinum, metals are not stable with respect to oxidation in air. The change in the Gibbs function for oxidation of a typical metal is large and negative. For instance,

---

[4] The Li^+ is effectively negative compared to the Ni^{2+} of the host structure.

$$Al + \tfrac{3}{2}O_2 \rightarrow \tfrac{1}{2}Al_2O_3 \qquad \Delta G°_{298} = -404.0\,kcal$$
$$Fe + \tfrac{1}{2}O_2 \rightarrow FeO \qquad \Delta G°_{298} = -68.0\,kcal$$
$$Ni + \tfrac{1}{2}O_2 \rightarrow NiO \qquad \Delta G°_{298} = -60.0\,kcal$$

These thermodynamic data indicate that the state of stable equilibrium of these metals exposed to air at 298°K is complete oxidation to solid oxides. Sometimes a piece of native copper is found, but except for the noble metals, the natural state of metals in the surface layers of the earth is almost always in chemical combination, with oxygen, sulfur, or other elements. When you stop to think of it, it is amazing that a highly reactive metal like aluminum or magnesium can be used at all as a structural material. We know in a general way the answer to this paradox—the metals become covered with layers of oxide which protect them from further attack by oxygen. Although the equilibrium condition would be complete oxidation, the rate of attainment of this equilibrium is often extremely slow.

The theory of the rate of growth of tarnish layers on metals was worked out by Carl Wagner about 1933. Although many details remain to be elucidated, the mechanisms that he set forth appear to be basically correct. Let us consider the oxidation of a sheet of pure nickel as a typical example. The stages in the oxidation process are summarized in Fig. 5.8.

First, an oxygen molecule strikes the clean, bare surface of nickel atoms and it is chemisorbed with dissociation into atoms which form strong Ni—O bonds with the underlying nickel. Soon the entire surface is covered with a layer of bonded oxygen atoms. Probably every nickel atom in the surface holds an oxygen atom. This reaction takes place rapidly even at temperatures as low as the boiling point of liquid nitrogen (78°K). With ordinary high-vacuum systems it is easy to reduce the pressure to about 10^{-7} torr (mm Hg). At this pressure, however, the rate at which gas molecules are striking the surface is so high that a clean surface of metal, for example, a freshly evaporated film, would be covered by an oxide layer one molecule thick (a *monolayer*) within a fraction of a second.

It is interesting to calculate the exact rate at which gas mole-

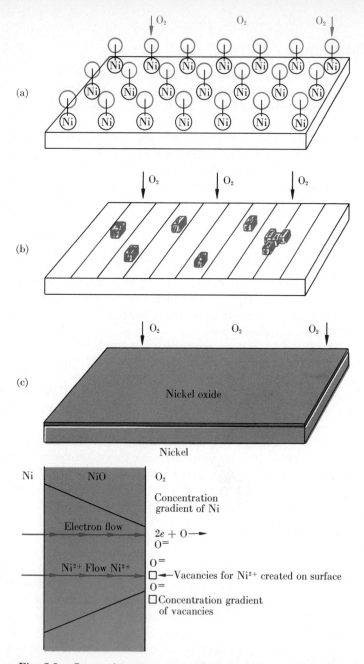

Fig. 5.8. Successive stages in oxidation of Ni. (a) O_2 molecules strike the surface, dissociate and form a monolayer chemisorbed. (b) Crystallites of NiO nucleate and grow laterally to cover the surface. (c) Ni ions diffuse outward through the NiO layer to react with attacking oxygen.

cules strike the surface. The formula derived from the kinetic theory of gases for the number of molecules striking unit area in unit time is

$$r = \frac{1}{4}N\bar{c} = \frac{1}{4}N\left(\frac{8RT}{\pi M}\right)^{1/2} \tag{5.8}$$

where N is number of molecules per cubic centimeter and $\bar{c}$ is the average speed of a gas molecule $[=(8RT/\pi M)^{1/2}$, where M is the molecular weight]. From the ideal gas equation, $PV = nRT$,

$$N = \frac{PVL}{RT} \tag{5.9}$$

where $L = 6.02 \times 10^{23}$, the number of molecules in a mole. With $R = 82.05$ cm^3 atm mole^{-1} and P in torr at 25°C,

$$N = \frac{(6.02 \times 10^{23})P}{82.05 \times 298 \times 760} = (3.24 \times 10^{16})P$$

For example, at 10^{-7} torr, $N = 3.24 \times 10^9$ cm^{-3}. The number of oxygen molecules striking unit area per second from Eq. (5.8) would be $r = 3.60 \times 10^{13}$.

We can estimate the number of Ni atoms exposed per square centimeter if we consider the planes of closest packing, that is, the 111 planes. The side of the unit cubic cell of Ni is $a_0 = 3.517$ Å so that the spacing between atoms in the closest-packed planes would be $a_0/2^{1/2} = 2.49$ Å. The area for a Ni atom would be 5.36 Å^2 and thus the number of Ni atoms per unit area in the surface is 1.86×10^{15} cm^{-2}. Although we calculated this number for the case of Ni, it is more or less the same for most crystals and we can think of 10^{15} sites cm^{-2} as a good average number for many surfaces.

When an O_2 molecule strikes a bare spot on the Ni surface, it dissociates to form a Ni—O bond about half the time. Even if it strikes a patch already occupied by O, it will generally dissociate and the oxygen atom will skitter over the surface until it finds a bare patch to combine with. With 3.60×10^{13} collisions per sec-cm^2 and 1.86×10^{15} sites per square centimeter we can estimate that it will take only about 52 seconds to cover the surface completely at 10^{-7} torr.

Such calculations proved that it would be simply impossible to measure properties of clean metal surfaces in conventional high-vacuum systems. Beginning about twenty years ago, Alpert (6) and others developed techniques for working at ultrahigh vacuums of 10^{-9} torr and below. We can now get a laboratory vacuum of 10^{-10} torr without unreasonable difficulty. At this pressure a clean metal surface would last about 7 hours before it was half-covered with oxygen.

So much for the first stage of oxidation. What happens next is a nucleation of tiny crystals of oxide apparently formed from the extended film covering the surface. These nuclei are the first bits of oxide to have the crystal structure of bulk oxide. Once the nuclei are formed they grow rapidly and soon cover the metal with a coherent layer of oxide which may be several hundred to a thousand angstroms thick.

A spectacular way to study the early stages of oxidation was invented by Alan Gwathmey (7). A *single crystal* of the metal was machined and electropolished to form an almost perfect sphere. On the surface of such a sphere many different possible crystal planes of the metal would simultaneously be exposed. When the sphere was placed in an oxidizing atmosphere at elevated temperature, oxide films grew at different rates on these different faces, to create a multicolored pattern of interference colors. Knowing the region on the sphere corresponding to each crystal face of the metal, Gwathmey could deduce from the interference color the thickness of the oxide formed on that face. Figure 5.9 shows the result of such an experiment in which a single-crystal sphere of Ni was oxidized at 400°C. The fastest oxidation was in the vicinity of the (100) face in the [011] zone, followed by the (310), (211), (100), and (111) faces in decreasing order. We do not yet have a satisfactory theory to explain these different oxidation rates at different crystal faces. What do you think the cause might be?

Further growth of oxide occurs more slowly. It is controlled by diffusion of reactants through the oxide layer. How do the Ni and O reactants reach each other across the layer of NiO? Either O can diffuse inward, or Ni ions diffuse outward. It turns out that in this case and most of the others so far studied metal ions and electrons move outward through the oxide layer to meet attacking

Fig. 5.9.   Oxidation of a spherical single crystal of Ni at 400°C and 30 torr.   (K. R. Lawless, University of Virginia.)

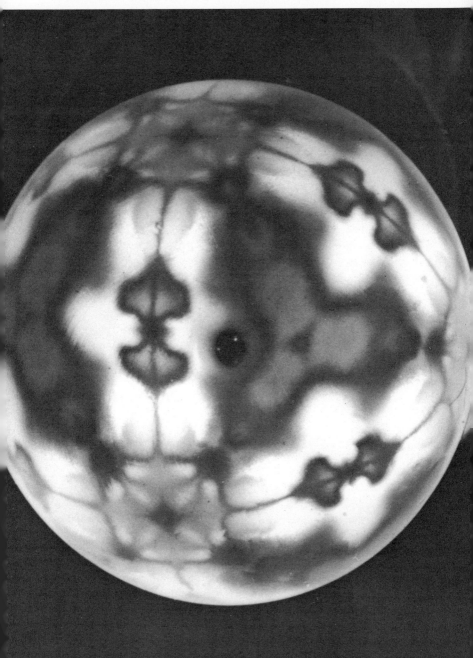

oxygen at the outer interface. The reason for this mechanism in the case of NiO is easy to see since the crystal can contain excess O and the resultant structure then has vacant Ni^{2+} sites. These vacant sites provide a convenient means for moving Ni^{2+} ions in the structure. They can move by jumping from occupied sites to vacant sites. Such a process is much easier than trying to push an interstitial O atom through the quite closely packed crystal. Electrons pass from the metal through the oxide layer and react with adsorbed oxygen atoms to yield oxide ions. The addition of oxide ions to the surface layer creates surface vacancies at potential Ni sites, and Ni ions can jump into these new vacant sites. The net result is equivalent to a flow of vacancies from the NiO/O_2 interface inward to the Ni/NiO interface, where the vacancies are annihilated by combination with Ni^{2+} ions from the metal. The elec·trons liberated in this step flow through the oxide layer to the outer surface where they can reduce more oxygen atoms.

In the case of oxidation of nickel occurring at temperatures above 200°C, the electrical conductivity is sufficiently high that electrons can pass rapidly through the NiO layer. (Actually, NiO is a positive-hole semiconductor but an inward flux of holes is equivalent to an outward flux of electrons.) In other cases, however, the oxide film on a metal is such a good insulator that electrons cannot get through at an appreciable rate and oxidation virtually ceases. Such is the case with aluminum at room temperature, where an insulating film of Al_2O_3 only about 40 Å thick affords effectively complete protection against further oxidation.

5.9   WAGNER THEORY OF TARNISHING

Let us derive the theoretical equation for the rate of growth of oxide layer for a case like that of the Ni oxidation in Fig. 5.8c, in which only the positive ions and the electrons are appreciably mobile in the oxide. A current of charged particles can quite generally be represented as the sum of two terms, one due to diffusion along a concentration gradient and the other due to motion in an electric field, E. With subscripts i referring to ions and e to electrons, we represent the concentrations as N_i, N_e (particles per cubic centimeter), the diffusion coefficients D_i, D_e (cm² sec⁻¹), and the mobilities (velocities per unit field) v_i, v_e. Thus, the fluxes (number flowing per second through one square centimeter) of ions and electrons can be written (with x the distance from the metal-to-oxide interface):

$$S_e = -D_e \frac{dN_e}{dx} - EN_e v_e$$

$$S_i = -D_i \frac{dN_i}{dx} + EN_i v_i$$

(5.10)

Electrodiffusion equations of this form are useful in many applications in which charged particles move through fields and concentration gradients. Note that the electrical terms have different signs in the two cases, since the charges have opposite signs.

We eliminate the field E between these two simultaneous Eqs. (5.10),

$$\frac{S_e}{N_e v_e} + \frac{S_i}{N_i v_i} = -\frac{D_e}{N_e v_e}\frac{dN_e}{dx} - \frac{D_i}{N_i v_i}\frac{dN_i}{dx}$$

In the steady state the currents of electrons and ions are equal, that is, effectively Ni *atoms* are moving across the layer, so that we can set $S_e = z_i S_i = S$, where $z_i = 2$ for the Ni²⁺ ions. We also make use of the Einstein relation between diffusion coefficients and mobilities,

$$\frac{D}{v} = \frac{kT}{ze}$$

(5.11)

Thus

$$S\left(\frac{1}{N_e v_e} + \frac{1}{z_i N_i v_i}\right) = -\frac{kT}{e}\left(\frac{1}{N_e}\frac{dN_e}{dx} + \frac{1}{N_i z_i}\frac{dN_i}{dx}\right) \quad (5.12)$$

The transference number t of a charged particle is the fraction of current carried by that particle in a conducting system. Thus, if σ is the conductivity

$$t_e \sigma = eN_e v_e$$
$$t_i \sigma = z_i eN_i v_i$$

In the case of NiO (since conductance by negative ions is negligible), $t_e + t_i = 1$. Hence, Eq. (5.12) becomes

$$S = \frac{-t_e t_i \sigma kT}{e^2} \left(\frac{1}{N_e} \frac{dN_e}{dx} + \frac{1}{z_i N_i} \frac{dN_i}{dx} \right) \tag{5.13}$$

We could apply this equation to calculate the flux of ions through the oxide layer for various special cases, and we shall consider Ni oxidation as a typical example. Stoichiometric NiO is an insulator, so that the flow of ions and electrons that causes the growth of the NiO layer is made possible by the departure of NiO from exact stiochiometry. The number of mobile electrons (or positive holes) is thus equal to the number of vacant cation sites (or mobile ions), so that in the growing oxide layer on Ni we can set

$$N_e = N_i = N$$

Equation (5.13) thus becomes, with $z_i = 2$,

$$S = \frac{-t_e t_i \sigma kT}{e^2} \frac{3}{2N} \frac{dN}{dx}$$

Also in NiO, $t_e \approx 1$, so that

$$S = \frac{-3 t_i \sigma kT}{2N e^2} \frac{dN}{dx}$$

or

$$S = -3D_i \frac{dN}{dx}$$

Integrating across the film we obtain[5]

$$S = 3D_i \frac{N_1 - N_0}{y}$$

where N_1 and N_0 are the concentration of Ni in NiO at the two interfaces, and y is the film thickness. The growth rate of thickness of oxide is the flux S (atoms per cm² sec) $\times$ the volume of crystalline NiO per Ni atom, V. Thus

$$\frac{dy}{dt} = \frac{3D_i V(N_1 - N_0)}{y} \tag{5.14}$$

---

[5] We assume that D_i is a constant, independent of N.

This equation can be compared with the experimental law of growth of the film which is

$$\frac{dy}{dt} = \frac{K}{y} \tag{5.15}$$

where K is called the *parabolic rate constant* for metal oxidation. Hence,

$$K = 3VD_i(N_1 - N_0) \tag{5.16}$$

As can be seen from the derivation, the factor 3 which occurs here is a consequence of the specific defect structure of NiO. It would be different for different types of nonstoichiometric oxides.

The rates of metal oxidation at high temperatures often follow Eq. (5.15). When Eq. (5.15) is integrated with the initial conditions $y = 0$ at $t = 0$, we obtain

$$y^2 = 2Kt \tag{5.17}$$

This is the equation of a parabola and indicates that if we plot the square of the film thickness versus the time, a straight line should be obtained. The rate constant K is usually given in units of cm^2 sec^{-1}. The oxidation of Ni from 400 to 1000°C is in good agreement with this "parabolic rate law." We may note, however, that the theoretical foundation of the "law" presupposes a coherent and adherent oxide film. If the oxide layer scales away from the metal, or if oxidation proceeds so rapidly that the region next to the metal develops porosity, the parabolic law may fail, and a catastrophic oxidation of the metal ensue, despite the best efforts of the oxide layer to provide protection. Resistance to high-temperature oxidation in technical applications may often therefore be primarily a question of how to achieve an adherent oxide layer, and less a matter of the electrical properties of the oxide that are emphasized by the theory (8,9).

REFERENCES

(1) N. F. Mott, "On the Transition to Metallic Conduction in Semiconductors," *Can. J. Phys.* **34**, 1356 (1956).

(2) H. G. Drickamer, *Science* **142**, 1429 (1963).

(3) E. Wigner and H. B. Huntington, *J. Chem. Phys.* **3**, 764 (1935).

(4) F. J. Morin, *Phys. Rev. Letters* **3**, 34 (1959).

(5) E. R. Schatz (ed.), *Transition Metal Compounds: Transport and Magnetic Properties* (New York: Gordon and Breach, 1964).

(6) D. Alpert, *J. Appl. Phys.* **24**, 860 (1953).

(7) F. W. Young, J. V. Cathcart, and A. T. Gwathmey, *Acta Met.* **4**, 145 (1956).

(8) O. Kubaschewski, *Oxidation of Metals and Alloys* (London: Butterworths, 1962).

(9) J. Bénard, *Oxydation des Métaux*, 2 vols. (Paris: Gauthier-Villars, 1962, 1964). (If you don't read French, you will still enjoy the pictures.)

VI

Ruby

THE FINEST RUBIES come from the Mogok region of northern Burma 150 km northeast of Mandalay. The most famous of these gems was Nga Mauk which belonged to the murderous King Thebaw of Burma. It was demanded by the British when they seized Burma in 1885 but the stone disappeared and has not been seen in public since that time. Burmese regard ruby as a sacred stone and perhaps Nga Mauk is still being worshipped in some mountain stronghold. Synthetic rubies are now made in Indiana. They differ from the natural stones in being more nearly perfect and much less expensive.

Our interest in ruby is not primarily due to its beauty as a gemstone but to its excellent performance in masers and lasers— devices for amplification of electromagnetic radiation. The signals from Telstar, our first communications satellite, were picked up through ruby microwave amplifiers, and the sharply focused flash of intense light with which a surgeon reseals a detached retina is provided by a ruby laser. Before we can discuss the operation of these important solid state devices we must study the structure of ruby and the origins of its electromagnetic spectra.

6.1 CRYSTAL STRUCTURE

Ruby is a species of corundum, α-Al_2O_3, colored red by dissolved chromium. Sapphire is a blue variety of the same crystal with color due to iron and (or) titanium. Corundum crystallizes in the rhombohedral (sometimes called trigonal) system, with the structure shown in Fig. 6.1a. You can look at this structure in the following way. Start with a cube and place Al_2O_3 units at its corners. Then stretch the cube along one of its body diagonals, a [111] direction. Finally, place another Al_2O_3 unit at the center of the rhombohedron so produced. The rhombohedral angle is $\alpha = 55°17'$ and the length of the unit cell $a_0 = 5.42$ Å. The unit cell contains two Al_2O_3 units ($Z = 2$).

Although we have described this structure in terms of Al_2O_3 units, no actual "molecules" of Al_2O_3 can be distinguished in the three-dimensional pattern. We can best visualize this pattern as an approximately hexagonal closest-packed array of oxide ions with Al^{3+} ions in some of the octahedral interstitial sites. There are enough such interstitial sites between each layer of O^{2-} ions to accommodate one Al^{3+} for each O^{2-}. In corundum, therefore, only two thirds of these sites can be filled. Parts of three such O^{2-} layers are shown in Fig. 6.1b with Al^{3+} ions nestling in their interstitial positions.

The exact coordination of an Al^{3+} ion is shown in Fig. 6.1c. We note that the octahedron of O^{2-} ions is far from regular. Three O^{2-} ions lie in a plane 1.37 Å from the Al^{3+} site, but the other three are in a plane only 0.80 Å from the Al^{3+}. The Al—O distances are 1.98 and 1.84 Å, respectively.

In ruby a small fraction of the Al^{3+} ions, from 0.04% in a pale pink specimen to 0.5% in a deep red one, are replaced by Cr^{3+} ions. Since their ionic charges are the same and the radius of Cr^{3+}

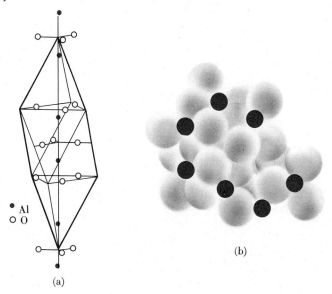

(a)

(b)

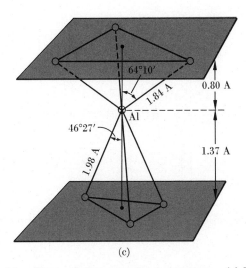

(c)

Fig. 6.1. Views of the corundum structure. (a) Unit cell of
a-Al_2O_3. (b) Packing of large oxide ions with Al^{3+} in interstices.
(c) Coordination of Al atom in a-Al_2O_3.

(0.69 Å) is not much greater than that of Al^{3+} (0.57Å), Cr^{3+} can replace small amounts of Al^{3+} without producing undue strains in the crystal.

6.2   GROWTH OF CRYSTALS

Synthetic ruby and sapphire are made by the *Verneuil* or *flame process* in the form of single crystals called *boules*. The apparatus used is shown in Fig. 6.2a, b. The starting material is a fine

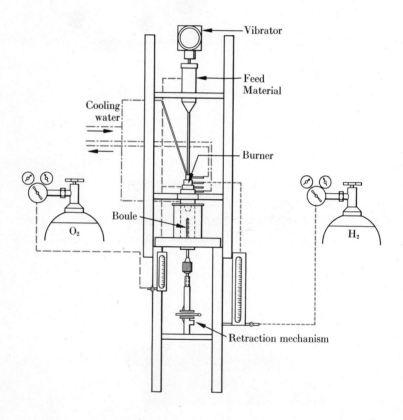

Fig. 6.2a. Apparatus for growing crystals by the Verneuil (flame) process. (Union Carbide Company.)

Fig. 6.2b. A furnace, showing a finished boule on its pedestal.

powder made by calcining alum $(NH_4Al(SO_4)_2 \cdot 12H_2O)$ with chromic oxide (Cr_2O_3) for ruby, or with oxides of iron and titanium for blue sapphire. The furnace uses an oxyhydrogen flame. The powder is kept in a hopper with a fine mesh screen at its base. As the hopper is tapped, powder feeds into the oxygen stream, which flows through the central tube of the burner. Hydrogen is supplied to the flame through an annular tube surrounding the oxygen tube. The flame is contained in a cylindrical ceramic muffle at the base of which is a pedestal whose height is adjusted with a screw. As the powder falls through the flame it builds up a mass of sintered crystal on the pedestal, from which a thin single-crystal rod of solidified melt emerges. The operating conditions are now changed to create a mushroom-shaped bulb at the top of the initial rod, and this grows to the diameter of the boule, further growth being maintained at constant diameter by slowly retracting the pedestal.

The boule must be carefully annealed to remove internal stresses introduced during growth. It is possible to produce well annealed single-crystal boules up to 2.0 cm diameter and 30 cm long. Ruby specimens of different shapes and sizes are cut from the boules with a diamond saw.

6.3   CRYSTAL FIELD THEORY

When a Cr^{3+} ion is placed at the center of the distorted octahedron of O^{2-} ions in the corundum structure, the electrons of Cr^{3+} are subjected to a strong electrostatic field due to the surrounding negative charges. The allowed energy levels of the Cr^{3+} ion are modified by this so-called *crystal field*. Transitions between these new energy levels give rise to many interesting features in the spectra of ruby.

Before we consider the effect of the crystal field on Cr^{3+}, let us review the energy levels of the Cr^{3+} ion as it would exist in isolation in a vacuum. Its electronic configuration is $1s^2 2s^2 2p^6 3s^2 3p^6 3d^3$, so that there are three $3d$ electrons outside a closed argon-type shell. Each electron moves in a field caused by attraction from the positive nuclear charge Z and repulsions from all the other negative electrons. The total energy H of an electron will include the sum of these two potential energy terms as well as the kinetic energy $p^2/2m$, where p is its momentum and m its mass. Thus,

$$H = \frac{p^2}{2m} - \frac{Ze^2}{r} + \Sigma \frac{e^2}{r_i} \qquad (6.1)$$

where r is distance of the electron from the nucleus, and r_i is distance of the given electron from another electron.

In addition to the electrostatic contributions to the potential energy, we must include another smaller term called the *spin-orbit interaction energy*. This term arises from the fact that the electrons have intrinsic spins and hence act as little magnets. The motion of an electron in its orbit, like a current in a coil of wire, also creates a magnetic field, so that an electron can have an orbital magnetic moment as well as its spin magnetic moment. The interaction between these two magnetic moments of an electron is the *spin-orbit interaction*. It adds to Eq. (6.1) an additional term, which can be written as

$$H_{so} = \lambda \mathbf{l} \cdot \mathbf{s} \qquad (6.2)$$

where $\mathbf{l}$ is the quantum number specifying orbital angular momentum, $\mathbf{s}$ is the spin quantum number, and λ is the *spin-orbit interaction constant*. The $\mathbf{l}$ and $\mathbf{s}$ are written as vectors to indicate that the interaction depends on the orientation of the two corresponding magnetic moments.[1] To consider spin-orbit interactions in the ion Cr^{3+} we can restrict our attention to the three $3d$ electrons, because all orbital and spin angular momenta due to the closed inner shells average to zero.

The different energy levels that can arise from the $3d^3$ configuration are shown in Fig. 6.3. They are classified as *quartet* and *doublet* terms depending on the value of the total spins of the three electrons. If all three spins are parallel:

$$\uparrow \ \uparrow \ \uparrow \qquad S = \tfrac{3}{2} \quad 2S + 1 = 4 \quad \text{(Quartets)}$$

---

[1] The dot or scalar product of the two vectors, written $\mathbf{l} \cdot \mathbf{s}$ is a scalar whose magnitude is $ls \cos \theta$, where θ is the angle between l and s. You can consider $s \cos \theta$ as the component of s in the direction of l.

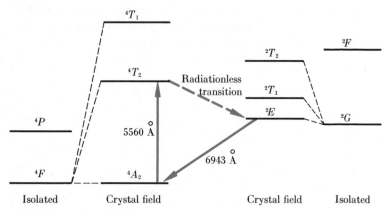

Fig. 6.3.   **The energy levels of Cr^{3+} in vacuum and as substituted for Al^{3+} in corundum.**

If only two of the spins are parallel:

$$\uparrow \ \downarrow \ \uparrow \qquad S = \tfrac{1}{2} \quad 2S + 1 = 2 \quad \text{(Doublets)}$$

The value of $2S + 1$ gives the *multiplicity* of the terms, which we can consider to be the number of ways in which the total spin S can be aligned in an external field.   The component of S in the field direction is specified by the quantum number M_S.   For example, for $S = \tfrac{3}{2}$, M_S can be $\tfrac{3}{2}$, $\tfrac{1}{2}$, $-\tfrac{1}{2}$, $-\tfrac{3}{2}$ (quartet); for $S = \tfrac{1}{2}$, M_S can be $\tfrac{1}{2}$ or $-\tfrac{1}{2}$ (doublet).

The state of lowest energy for Cr^{3+}, the *ground state*, is a quartet denoted by ^4F.   In accord with *Hund's rule*, for a given electronic configuration (such as $3d^3$) the state of highest multiplicity will be the ground state, because when the electrons have their spins parallel, their spin quantum numbers are identical and they are forced by the Pauli exclusion principle to avoid each other, so that repulsion between electrons, which raises the energy, is kept as low as possible.

In the absence of a magnetic field the spin-orbit interaction will produce a small splitting of the terms of ^4F and other multiplet states.   For the sake of simplicity, this fine structure is not shown in Fig. 6.3.

Suppose we now substitute the Cr^{3+} for an Al^{3+} ion inside the crystal, at the center of a distorted octahedron of O^{2-} ions. Let the energy of interaction with the crystal field be V_{cf}. How does V_{cf} compare in magnitude with the various terms that comprise the energy of the free ion? If V_{cf} is much smaller than these terms, the effect of the field will be only a slight modification of the energy levels of the free ion, and we should expect the spectra of the ion in the crystal to resemble those of the gaseous ion. On the other hand, if V_{cf} is about equal to or greater than the energy terms of the free ion, the energy levels and spectra of the ion must be profoundly modified by the crystal field.

In practice, three different situations are found in different substances: (1) $V_{cf} \gg e^2/r_i$, typical of complexes in which new chemical bonds, predominantly covalent in character, are formed between the surrounding ligands and the central ion. An example is ferricyanide ion. The Fe—C bonds change completely the energy states of the d electrons of Fe^{3+} in $[Fe(CN)_6]^{3-}$. (2) $V_{cf} \ll e^2/r_i$ and $\lambda \mathbf{l} \cdot \mathbf{s}$. In such cases the electrons of the central ion are so well shielded that interaction with the crystal field is small even compared to the spin-orbit interaction. Such is the situation of the rare earth ions, in which the $4f$ electrons, which form an incomplete inner shell, have nearly the same energies in the crystal as in the gaseous state. (3) The situation of Cr^{3+} in ruby is midway between these two extremes. The crystal field V_{cf} is larger than the spin-orbit interaction but considerably smaller than the interaction between electrons,

$$\frac{e^2}{r_i} > V_{cf} > \lambda \mathbf{l} \cdot \mathbf{s} \tag{6.3}$$

The effect of the crystal field on the lowest quartet level ^4F and the lowest doublet ^2P of an isolated Cr^{3+} is shown in Fig. 6.3. The transition between the ground state $^4A_2$ and the excited $^4T_2$ state corresponds to a wavelength of 5560 Å, in the green region of the spectrum. The light transmitted through the crystal is therefore red. The color of ruby is thus explained by a transition between two levels of the $3d^3$ electrons which originated from the ^4F ground state and were split by the crystal field. The transition is allowed since the two states have the same number of unpaired spins.

Spectral transitions between states with different spins are extremely unlikely, hence there is no absorption band corresponding to a transition from the ^4A to ^2E levels.

6.4   LASER ACTION

The word laser is an acronym for "Light Amplification by Stimulated Emission of Radiation." To understand how a laser lases, we must first review a few basic facts about absorption and emission of radiation.

When a Cr^{3+} ion in ruby absorbs a quantum of light at wavelength $\lambda = 5560$ Å it makes a transition from $^4A_2$ to $^4T_2$ state. The energy difference between these states is

$$E = h\nu_{12} = \frac{hc}{\lambda} = \frac{(6.62 \times 10^{-34})(3.0 \times 10^8)}{(5560 \times 10^{-10})} = 3.58 \times 10^{-19} \text{ joule}$$

Normally, in the absence of radiation at 5560 Å, almost all the Cr^{3+} centers in a piece of ruby would be in the ground state $^4A_2$. The energy difference between $^4A_2$ and $^4T_2$ is so big that the fraction of centers in the excited state would be negligibly small under conditions of thermal equilibrium. At 300°K this fraction would be $\exp(-E/kT) = \exp(-3.58 \times 10^{-19}/1.37 \times 10^{-23} \times 300) = e^{-87}$.

As the beam of light at 5560 Å passes through a ruby, the number of Cr^{3+} centers per cubic centimeter excited from $^4A_2$ to $^4T_2$ per second is given by

$$\frac{-dN_1}{dt} = B_{12}\rho(\nu_{12})N_1 \tag{6.4}$$

where N_1 is the number per cubic centimeter in the ground state [1] and ρ_{12} is the density of radiation (quanta per square centimeter-second) at the wavelength of the absorption line. The factor B_{12} is the *Einstein coefficient for absorption of radiation*.

The ions in the excited state may be stimulated to emit a quantum $h\nu_{12}$ by the electromagnetic field of the incident light beam. This induced emission depopulates the excited state [2] at a rate

$$\frac{-dN_2}{dt} = B_{21}\rho(\nu_{12})N_2 \tag{6.5}$$

where B_{21} is the *Einstein coefficient for induced (stimulated) emission of radiation.* The quantum-mechanical expression for the transition probabilities shows that $B_{12} = B_{21}$.[2]

Besides the induced emission of radiation, given by Eq. (6.5), an excited state will emit quanta spontaneously (that is, in absence of radiation at ν_{12}) at a rate of

$$\frac{-dN_2}{dt} = A_{21}N_2 \tag{6.6}$$

where A_{21} is the *Einstein coefficient for spontaneous emission.* On integration, Eq. (6.6) gives

$$N_2 = N_2{}^\circ \exp(-A_{21}t) = N_2{}^\circ \exp\left(\frac{-t}{\tau}\right) \tag{6.7}$$

where $\tau = A_{21}{}^{-1}$ is the *natural lifetime* of the excited state.

In an equilibrium state the rate at which centers are being excited is just equal to the rate at which excited states are returning to the ground state by *both* spontaneous and induced emissions. Thus

$$B_{12}N_1\rho(\nu_{12}) = A_{21}N_2 + B_{12}N_2\rho(\nu_{12}) \tag{6.8}$$

By the Boltzmann formula,

$$N_2 = N_1 \exp\left(\frac{-h\nu_{12}}{kT}\right)$$

Hence, from Eq. (6.8),

$$R = \frac{A_{21}}{B_{12}\rho(\nu_{12})} = \exp\left(\frac{h\nu_{12}}{kT}\right) - 1 \tag{6.9}$$

This equation gives the ratio of the rates of spontaneous and stimulated emissions.

In the optical region of the spectrum, stimulated emission is usually negligible compared to spontaneous emission. For in-

---

[2] A good discussion is given in (1). B_{12} is the probability that a photon will be absorbed *if* it strikes a system in the ground state, and B_{21} is the probability that a photon will cause emission from the excited to a ground state *if* it strikes a system in the excited state. These *probabilities* must be equal, but of course at equilibrium there are far fewer systems in the excited state.

stance, in the case of the ruby line at 5560 Å, $R \approx \exp(h\nu/kT) \approx 10^{35}$ at 300°K. On the other hand, at lower frequencies, in the microwave region for example, R becomes much smaller. From Eq. (6.9) we see that R becomes equal to unity when the frequency

$$\nu_{12} = \frac{kT}{h} \ln 2 = 2.9 \times 10^{13} \text{ sec}^{-1} \text{ at } 300° \text{ K}$$

This is a frequency in the infrared region.

From Eqs. (6.8) and (6.9) we can see that in order to have the rate of emission of light greater than the rate of absorption, the right side of Eq. (6.8) must exceed the left side. This condition could be achieved only by a *population inversion*, which would cause N_2 to be greater than N_1 contrary to the normal Boltzmann distribution.

The energy states of Cr^{3+} in ruby, shown in Fig. 6.3, possess some rather unusual properties that make such a population inversion possible under certain conditions. As the Cr^{3+} centers absorb light in the 5560 Å band, they pass from the $^4A_2$ to the $^4T_2$ state, and an enhanced concentration of these excited states results. Most of the energy absorbed by ruby at 5560 Å is not simply reemitted at this same wavelength. Although the spontaneous emission coefficient is quite high, there is a yet more rapid process, a *radiationless transition* to the ^2E state. This transition is said to be *phonon assisted*, because it is made possible by uptake of energy into vibrations of the crystal structure. We note that the rate of transition $^4T_2 \rightarrow {}^4A_2$ is $3 \times 10^5 \text{ sec}^{-1}$, but for $^4T_2 \rightarrow {}^2E$ it is considerably higher, $2 \times 10^7 \text{ sec}^{-1}$. Thus most of the optical excitation energy pours over into this ^2E state.

Now the ^2E state is metastable with respect to the $^4A_2$ ground state, since *optical* transitions between doublets and quartets are extremely slow, owing to the change in total spins. The spontaneous emission coefficient in this case is only $2 \times 10^2 \text{ sec}^{-1}$ and ^2E has a long natural lifetime. The wavelength of the transition $^2E \rightarrow {}^4A_2$ would be 6943 Å, a bright red line.

If sufficient power is pumped into the $^4A_2 \rightarrow {}^4T_2$ transition, we can produce a concentration of the metastable ^2E states much higher than that given by the Boltzmann equation, that is, a definite population inversion.

Suppose now that such a population inversion has been achieved and the ^2E states are loaded far beyond their Boltzmann or equilibrium capacities. The first condition necessary to achieve light amplification has thus been achieved, a population inversion in an appropriate excited state. The second necessary condition is that an experimental arrangement be designed in which the induced emission of light is greater than the losses from the system due to absorption, scattering, and other mechanisms. Such losses are usually expressed in terms of the value of Q for the oscillation process, defined as 2π times the number of periods T_0 that the oscillation lasts before its total energy has decreased to $1/e$ of its initial value. Thus,

$$Q = 2\pi\left(\frac{\tau}{T_0}\right) = 2\pi\nu_0\tau$$

where ν_0 is the frequency and τ the decay time to $1/e$ of initial energy. If a sufficiently high Q can be achieved together with population inversion in the ruby, a small input of red light can cause a much higher output.

If such a system is exposed to *red light* at 6943 Å, the induced emission, which depends on the radiation density, will increase rapidly. There will be a burst of red light as the ^2E states revert to the ground state by the stimulated emission process. Light amplification would then be accomplished and the ruby would "lase."

6.5 EXPERIMENTAL SETUP OF LASER

The first ruby laser was invented by Maiman in 1960 (2). In outline, the experimental setup is shown in Fig. 6.4a. A cylindrical ruby was placed at the axis of a helical flash tube, which was mounted in a reflecting cylinder lined with magnesia. One flat end of the crystal was coated with an opaque reflecting layer of silver, and the other end coated with a thinner layer of silver, which transmitted about one third of the light incident upon it. The flash had an energy of about 3000 joules causing almost instantaneous population inversion of the ^2E with respect to the ground state. The emission line at 6943 Å (14,400 cm^{-1}) was reflected back and forth between the silver mirrors causing stimulated emission from the ^2E

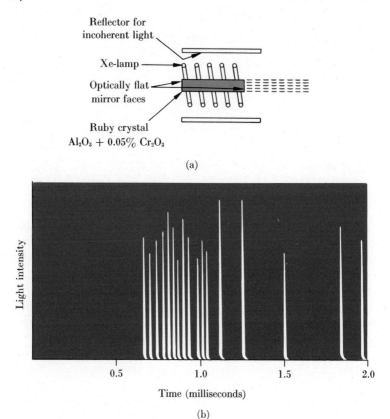

(a)

(b)

Fig. 6.4.   (a) Ruby laser of T. H. Maiman.   (b) Light output from directly excited ruby laser.

state at each passage.   The Q of this device was sufficiently high to allow a net amplification of the energy in the oscillations.   The newly emitted light would in turn cause more stimulated emission, so that the rate of emission would build up rapidly, and the output would appear in a series of sharp spikes, as shown in Fig. 6.4b.

The energy emitted in the output beam I_e is related to the energy in the reflected standing wave I_s by

$$I_e = \frac{T}{A + T} I_s \qquad (6.10)$$

where A is the absorbance and T the transmittance of the semire-flective film. For silver in the red region of the spectrum $A = 0.035$ and $T = 0.020$. The resultant rather high energy absorption in the film caused it to heat and shatter in the early lasers. Later developments have led to improved coatings for the crystal ends.

The power emitted in the spikes of laser output amounted to tens of megawatts, yet the overall line width of the red light was less than 0.0001 cm^{-1}. Never before had such intense, coherent, and sharply monochromatic light pulses been available. It should be noted, however, that the device did not provide *continuous* light amplification. Many applications were soon made of this new light source. For example, the laser spike can be used to photograph rapidly moving objects, such as a bullet traveling at 200 m sec^{-1}. It is useful in micrography of living organisms, since the problem of movement of the object is overcome and there is no chromatic aberration. So well defined is the beam that a pulse of light from a ruby laser has been reflected from the surface of the moon and the reflection picked up and amplified at the surface of the earth.

The *coherence* of the radiation emitted by lasers may be even more important than its intensity (3). A beam of radiation is co-herent if successive sections of its wave train are in phase. For ex-ample, absorption of light is a coherent process. The sinusoidal wave representing the beam of radiation is reduced in amplitude on passing through an absorber, but the phase relations between dif-ferent parts of the wave are not disturbed. The stimulated emis-sion of a laser is just the reverse of absorption, the amplitude of the emitted wave is increased but its phase is coherent. On the other hand, spontaneous emission is a random process, the phases of the waves corresponding to successive quanta emitted are not at all coherent. With respect to signal amplification, such spontaneous emission would be worse than useless—it would constitute "noise."

Some of the most remarkable applications of lasers may be in communications. The information-carrying capacity of a highly coherent optical source is amazingly high. For example, a carrier wave frequency of $\nu = 10^{14}$ sec^{-1} could provide 10^{10} channels each

10 kc sec^{-1} wide. This arrangement would allow half the world's population to hold simultaneously high-fidelity conversations with the other half, while leaving 9×10^9 channels still unused.

6.6 PARAMAGNETIC IONS IN MAGNETIC FIELDS

In Section 6.3 the ground state of Cr^{3+} in ruby was described as a quartet ($^4A_2$). This means that the *multiplicity* $2S + 1 = 4$ where S is the total spin. Therefore, $S = \frac{3}{2}$ indicating that the three $3d$ electrons have spins parallel.

In 1896 Paul Zeeman showed that lines in atomic spectra could be split into closely spaced multiplets if the source of the spectra (a discharge tube, for example) was placed in a magnetic field. The origin of this Zeeman effect can be understood in general terms as follows.

In the absence of any external field there is no particular direction of physical significance for an atom in a vacuum. The application of an external magnetic field, however, at once provides an axis in space with a definite directional character. The magnetic field also exerts a force on the little magnets of the spinning electrons in the atom. We say that the magnetic moment of the atom is *coupled* to the external magnetic field.

A situation analogous to this is familiar to every person who has played with a top. A spinning top is subject to an external field with a definite direction, the gravitational field directed toward the center of the earth. We can denote the angular momentum of the top by a vector along the axis of rotation, and this angular momentum is *coupled* to the external gravitational field, which exerts a torque perpendicular to the rotation axis and the direction of the field. As a consequence, the top acquires a motion in which its axis of spin (angular momentum vector) *precesses* about the direction of the external field.

An atom or ion with a total spin S placed in a magnetic field is similar to a spinning top placed in a gravitational field. The spin angular momentum vector (or the magnetic moment vector which is aligned with it) is coupled to the external magnetic field so that it must precess about the field direction. The spin quantum number S corresponds to a spin angular momentum of magnitude,

$$P_s = \left(\frac{h}{2\pi}\right)[S(S+1)]^{1/2} \tag{6.11}$$

The magnetic moment μ_s is proportional to the spin angular momentum P_s,

$$\frac{\mu_s}{P_s} = \gamma = -g_s \frac{e}{2mc} \tag{6.12}$$

Note that the direction of the magnetic moment is opposite to that of the spin angular momentum because of the negative charge of the electron. The proportionality factor γ is called the *magnetogyric ratio*. For free electrons $g_s = 2.0023$, but it may differ for electrons in a paramagnetic ion.[3]

We expect any periodic motion in an atom to be quantized, and precession of magnetic moment about an external field is no exception. The quantization rule is that the component of angular momentum in the field direction z can have only the values,

$$P_{sz} = M_S \frac{h}{2\pi} \tag{6.13}$$

where $M_S = S, S-1, \ldots, -S$. In the case of Cr^{3+} with $S = \frac{3}{2}$, therefore, $M_S = \frac{3}{2}, \frac{1}{2}, -\frac{1}{2}, -\frac{3}{2}$. The allowed components of the angular momentum are shown in Fig. 6.5. As a consequence only certain discrete frequencies ν are allowed for the precession of angular momentum about the external magnetic field, and the energy levels of the electron-spin system in the magnetic field are quantized. The energy of a magnetic dipole of moment μ_z in the direction of a field H_0 is $E = -\mu_z H_0$, and from Eqs. (6.12) and (6.13) the allowed energy levels are

---

[3] In the discussion that follows in this section, we consider that the magnetic properties of Cr^{3+} are due entirely to the electron spins. Thus we neglect the magnetic moment contributed by the orbital motions of the electrons and the resultant spin-orbit interactions, which would cause the effective g to deviate from the spin-only value.

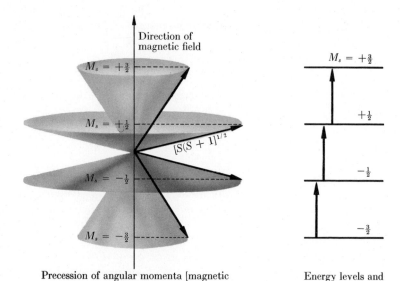

Precession of angular momenta [magnetic   Energy levels and
moments] about external magnetic field   allowed transitions

Fig. 6.5. **Quantization of total spin angular momentum for**
$S = \frac{3}{2}$ **(case of isolated Cr^{3+} ion).**

$$E = -\gamma P_z H_0 = -\gamma M_S \left(\frac{h}{2\pi}\right) H_0$$

$$= g_s \left(\frac{eh}{4\pi mc}\right) M_S H_0 \quad = g_s \beta M_S H_0 \quad (6.14)$$

where $\beta = (eh/4\pi mc)$ is the *Bohr magneton*.

Transitions between these energy levels correspond to absorption or emission of electromagnetic radiation. For example, with the usual selection rule, $\Delta M_S = \pm 1$,

$$h\nu = \Delta E = g_s \beta H_0 \quad\quad\quad\quad (6.15)$$

For $H_0 = 5000$ gauss, the frequency of the spectral line would be

$$\nu = \frac{g_s \beta H_0}{h} = \frac{(2.0032)(0.9273 \times 10^{-20})(5000)}{6.62 \times 10^{-27}} = 14.0 \text{ Gc sec}^{-1}$$

This frequency lies in the microwave region of the spectrum. We shall show somewhat later that the Zeeman levels of Cr^{3+} in ruby are suitable for amplification of radiation in this region of the spectrum. They can be used to construct a *maser* (for "Microwave Amplification by Stimulated Emission of Radiation").

6.7 COMBINED MAGNETIC AND CRYSTAL FIELDS—
THE SPIN HAMILTONIAN

We have described how a magnetic field splits the energy levels in the ground state of an isolated ion of Cr^{3+}. When Cr^{3+} is dissolved in ruby, however, the problem is more complex, since even before the magnetic field is applied, the electrostatic crystal field has provided an axis of quantization for the orbital angular momenta and spins. Thus the exact direction of the external magnetic field relative to the symmetry axis of this electrostatic field must be considered. Experimentally, therefore, we can expect that the observed splitting of energy levels will depend on the orientation of the crystal in the magnetic field. This "complication," however, is one reason why transition ions in crystals are so important in applications such as masers. It is possible by adjusting the magnetic field and its orientation to adjust the spacings of the energy levels over a considerable range, and thereby to obtain particular sets of levels most useful for various applications.

When we consider the situation of Cr^{3+} in a combined magnetic and crystal field, we find three energy terms of about the same order of magnitude:

    (a) the noncubic part of the crystal field, V_{nc}, that is, the part due to distortion of a regular octahedral configuration of O^{2-} ions, which was shown in Fig. 6.1;

    (b) the spin-orbit interaction V_{so};

    (c) the energy due to the external magnetic field V_H.

A complete theoretical treatment of the effects of these terms on the energy levels of Cr^{3+} would be beyond the capabilities of contemporary quantum mechanics, although good progress is constantly being made. The general pattern of the resultant energy levels can, however, be predicted and the spacings measured experimentally. The results are shown in Fig. 6.6. The combined effects of the noncubic field and the spin-orbit interaction split the

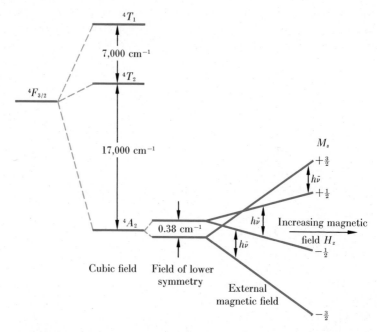

**Fig. 6.6. Splitting of the $^4F_{3/2}$ energy level of Cr^{3+} by internal
electric crystal fields of different symmetry and by an external
magnetic field.**

ground state into a closely spaced doublet. Then the magnetic
field splits each of these levels into two more, thus yielding the four
levels to be expected when all degeneracy[4] has been removed. At
small magnetic field strengths, we should not expect these levels to
be similar to those for electron spins in an isolated Cr^{3+} ion, but at
higher fields the levels can be assigned the quantum numbers
$M_S = \frac{3}{2}, \frac{1}{2}, -\frac{1}{2}, -\frac{3}{2}$, just as in the isolated ion, and thus become
spaced in the same order.

A convenient method has been devised for representing the

---

[4] *Degeneracy* means the existence of *more than one* distinct wave function
(quantum state) ψ having the same energy E.

energy levels of paramagnetic ions in crystals under the combined influence of spin-orbit interactions, noncubic crystal fields, and external magnetic fields. The three terms in the energy operator,[5]

$$\mathcal{H} = V_{nc} + V_{so} + V_H$$

are recast into the form of spin-component operators and magnetic field components in the x, y, z directions, to give an expression known as the *spin Hamiltonian*. The parameters in this expression depend on the strength and symmetry of the crystal field and on the spin-orbit coupling in the ion considered. Thus the spin Hamiltonian provides the most convenient way of comparing different ions in the same crystal field or a given ion in crystals with various fields. Once its parameters are known, the spin Hamiltonian can be used to calculate the energy levels at any field strength and crystal orientation. For an ion in a distorted octahedral field, a typical form of spin Hamiltonian would be

$$\mathcal{H} = g_{\parallel} H_z S_z + g_{\perp}(H_x S_x + H_y S_y) + D[S_z^2 - \tfrac{1}{3}S(S + 1)] \\ + E(S_x^2 - S_y^2) \quad (6.16)$$

Here the z axis is taken to coincide with the trigonal axis of the rhombohedron. H_x, H_y, H_z are components of the magnetic field in the directions of the three perpendicular axes, and S_x, S_y, S_z are the spin operators for the components of the spin. The parameter D measures the distortion of the octahedral field along the axial directions, forming the rhombohedron shown in Fig. 6.1c for the case of Cr^{3+} in corundum. The parameter E, in the "orthorhombic term," measures the distortion of the field in the x and y directions. For example, suppose there was a greater positive charge above the Cr^{3+} ion than below—it would then be pushed downward below the center of the octahedron and the resultant crystal field would have orthorhombic symmetry. In the case of Cr^{3+} in ruby, $S = \tfrac{3}{2}$ and it turns out the $g_{\parallel} = 1.9840$, $g_{\perp} = 1.9867$, $D = -5.747$ Gc sec^{-1} and $E = 0$.

---

[5] In quantum mechanics, observable quantities, such as energy, are formulated as operators, which operate upon wave functions ψ to give allowed sets of values for the quantity to be observed. For example, the equation $\mathcal{H}\psi_n = E_n\psi_n$ gives the energy level E_n corresponding to the wave function ψ_n.

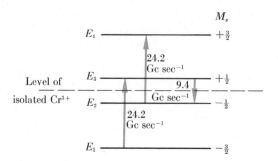

Fig. 6.7.   Energy levels of Cr^{3+} in ruby suitable for push-pull maser operation.

6.8   MASER ACTION OF RUBY

Certain energy levels of Cr^{3+} in ruby in a strong magnetic field are ideally suited for use in a maser.   Figure 6.7 shows the energy levels when the magnetic field is set at 4.2 kilogauss and an angle of 54.7° to the z axis of the crystal field.[6]   When a "pumping frequency" of 24.2 Gc sec^{-1} is employed, the transitions $E_1 \rightarrow E_3$ and $E_2 \rightarrow E_4$ both occur.   Consequently, E_2 is depleted and E_3 is filled by the same pumping frequency.   The result is a marked inversion of the population of level E_3 with respect to E_2.   Such an effect is called a "push-pull operation."   The signal frequency of the ruby maser in this mode of operation is 9.4 Gc sec^{-1}, which arises as stimulated emission of transitions between states E_3 and E_2.

In operation of a maser the crystal is usually cooled to liquid-helium temperature in order to minimize spin-lattice interaction and thereby sharpen the lines.   The crystal is mounted in a resonant cavity and power is fed in and taken out through wave guides. The cavity must be specially designed in view of the different frequencies of the input and output microwave oscillations.

---

[6] The cosine of this angle is $3^{-1/2}$ and for this particular value, it can be shown that the spin Hamiltonian of Eq. (6.16) leads to equal spacings of the pairs of levels E_2, E_3 and E_1, E_4 above and below the unperturbed level.

6.9 ELECTRON PARAMAGNETIC RESONANCE

Transitions between energy levels of paramagnetic ions in crystals are usually studied by a method called electron paramagnetic resonance (EPR) or electron spin resonance (ESR). This technique has become one of the most useful ways to study the details of crystal fields surrounding paramagnetic ions, color centers and labile reaction products in crystals (4). An outline of an experimental apparatus for EPR measurements is shown in Fig. 6.8a. The crystal is mounted in a waveguide cavity between the poles of a strong electromagnet. Microwave radiation is generated with a klystron and pumped through a waveguide into the cavity where a

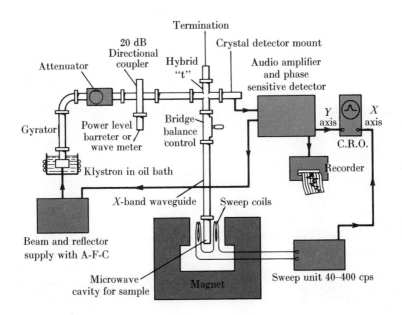

Fig. 6.8a. **Block diagram of X-band EPR spectrometer.** (Varian Instrument Co.)

standing-wave magnetic field pattern is set up. Figure 6.8b shows
the standing-wave pattern of this microwave magnetic field in a
typical waveguide used in an X-band EPR spectrometer. The
field of the strong magnet is varied gradually until a setting is
reached at which the natural precession frequency of the resultant
electron spin of the paramagnetic ion just matches the fixed microwave magnetic-field frequency. This is the condition of resonance
at which energy is absorbed from the microwave field by the spin
system. Generally, the klystron operates in the X band at 9.5 Gc
sec^{-1} (3.2 cm) or K band at 30 Gc sec^{-1} (1.25 cm). The magnetic
field is modulated by passing 50 c sec^{-1} current through coils cir-
cling the pole pieces, so that it is possible to sweep back and forth
through the resonant frequency and display the absorption line on
a cathode-ray oscilloscope.

At resonance, a quantum $h\nu$ of microwave radiation just
equals the spacing between two energy levels of the spin system.

**Fig. 6.8b. Microwave magnetic fields in TE$_{012}$ mode. (Varian
Instrument Co.)**

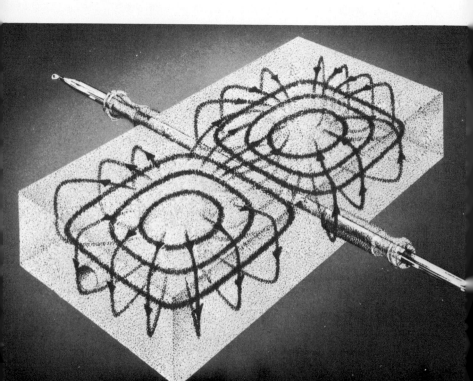

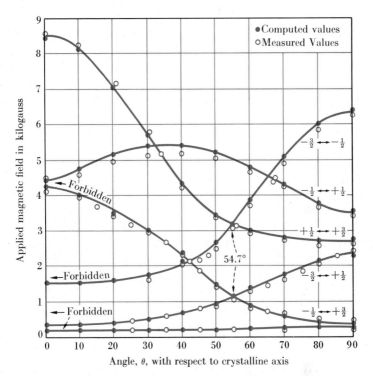

Fig. 6.9. Paramagnetic resonance spectra of Cr³⁺ in ruby at 12.33 Gc sec⁻¹, Schulz-Du Bois (5). (The magnetic field at peak of absorption line is plotted against the angle between the field and the 3-fold axis of the crystal.)

We often represent this resonance condition in terms of an empirical g value, given by

$$h\nu = g\beta H_0 \qquad (6.17)$$

When ν is in Gc sec⁻¹ and H_0 in kilogauss,

$$\nu = 1.3997\, g H_0$$

In operation of the EPR spectrometer, the magnetic field is changed at a constant rate so as to scan the different resonant conditions.   At resonance, energy is absorbed in the cavity, thus changing the signal being reflected back into the waveguide.   The level of this signal is monitored by a crystal detector and audio-amplifier and displayed on an oscilloscope which is swept at the 50 c sec^{-1} modulation frequency of the magnetic field.   Thus the shape of the absorption line can be seen on the scope.   A permanent record can be taken with a chart recorder.

Figure 6.9 shows spectra obtained for ruby at a frequency 12.33 Gc sec^{-1} with the magnetic field at various angles to the trigonal axis of the crystal.   The values of the magnetic field for the various transitions as computed from the spin Hamiltonian of Eq. (6.16) are shown together with the experimental values.   The agreement is excellent, and the spin Hamiltonian is in fact the accepted way of reporting results of EPR measurements.   We may note that in a strong crystal field, the selection rule $\Delta M_S = \pm 1$ is not obeyed and thus "forbidden" transitions are usually observed, though sometimes with lower intensities than "allowed" transitions.

REFERENCES

(1) W. Kauzmann, *Quantum Chemistry* (New York: Academic Press, 1957), p. 637.

(2) T. H. Maiman, *Nature* **187**, 493 (1960).

(3) O. S. Heavens, *Optical Masers* (London: Methuen, 1964), Chapter 2.

(4) G. E. Pake, *Paramagnetic Resonance* (New York: Benjamin, 1962).

(5) E. O. Schulz-Du Bois, "Paramagnetic Spectra of Substituted Sapphires," *Bell System Tech. J.* **38**, 271 (1959).

VII

Anthracene

Oᴜʀ ꜰɪʀꜱᴛ ꜱɪx solid states have been inorganic crystals and several more of that kind might well have been included: ice with its hydrogen bonds and high proton mobility, cadmium sulfide as a phosphor used in television screens, silica with its colorful geologic forms and industrial applications in ceramics and catalysis. Yet we could not entirely neglect the vast field of organic crystals with its great theoretical and practical importance. No single organic solid exemplifies all the properties of interest, but anthracene stands out because of the good quantitative work that has been done on single crystals of carefully purified material.

Electrical properties of organic crystals may be related to important biological mechanisms. Enhanced interest in the organic solid state was kindled by Szent-Györgyi (1) in 1941 when he suggested that certain intracellular organelles might function as semiconductors. Arrangements of large molecules in living cells may not be strictly crystalline but they often display structural order to a high degree. For example, chlorophyll is stacked in parallel layers in the chloroplasts of green plants, so that if a quantum of light is absorbed anywhere in the array, the excitation can move quickly to a site at which a photosynthetic reaction step occurs. The enzymes in mitochondria are arranged on internal membranes so that electron transport can perhaps facilitate oxidative phosphorylation processes in these organelles, which have been called the "power houses of living cells." A final example may be the mysterious sensory-receptor mechanism in the retina, through which absorption of a single light quantum can initiate an electrical impulse of about 50 mV along an optic nerve fiber.

7.1 STRUCTURE OF ANTHRACENE

Naphthalene and anthracene were among the first organic crystals whose structures were determined by x-ray methods. The large planar molecules are stacked in the crystals in such a way that a fair idea of their orientations could be deduced simply from the unit cell dimensions. More recently, refined x-ray analyses of the structures have been reported (2), so that the exact intermolecular arrangements as well as intramolecular bond distances and angles are known with remarkable accuracy.

The crystal structure of anthracene is depicted in Fig. 7.1. It is based on a monoclinic unit cell, with $a = 8.56$ Å, $b = 6.04$ Å, $c = 11.16$ Å, $\beta = 124.7°$. There are two molecules of anthracene per unit cell ($Z = 2$). We can think of a reference molecule placed so that its center of symmetry is at (000). The center of the second molecule is then at $(\frac{1}{2}\frac{1}{2}0)$. The molecule is planar to within about ± 0.01 Å, but high precision x-ray work has detected small deviations from exact planarity which can be directly related to forces exerted on a molecule by other molecules packed closely around it in the crystal. The structure is in fact approximately a closest-packed arrangement with each molecule having twelve nearest neighbors. The molecule at (000) is surrounded by six neighbors in the 001 plane with centers at (010), (0$\bar{1}$0), $(\frac{1}{2}\frac{1}{2}0)$,

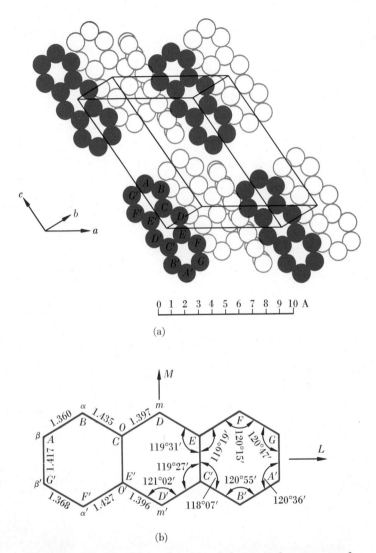

0 1 2 3 4 5 6 7 8 9 10 A

(a)

(b)

Fig. 7.1. Results of investigation of the crystal structure of anthracene. (a) Molecular arrangement in the unit cell. (b) Carbon-carbon distances and angles. (c) Model showing a layer of closely packed molecules in *ab* plane (Professor H. Pick). [Part (c) is on p. 192.]

$(\bar{\tfrac{1}{2}}\tfrac{1}{2}0)$, $(\tfrac{1}{2}\bar{\tfrac{1}{2}}0)$, and $(\bar{\tfrac{1}{2}}\bar{\tfrac{1}{2}}0)$. The upper end of the central molecule is wedged between three molecules at (001), $(\tfrac{1}{2}\tfrac{1}{2}1)$, and $(\tfrac{1}{2}\bar{\tfrac{1}{2}}1)$ and its lower end is similarly situated with respect to the layer below.[1] Anthracene usually crystallizes in flakes in which {001} planes form the well-developed surfaces. The nearest distances between molecules are all less than 3.0 Å, and are mostly H to H distances between neighboring molecules. The only carbon atoms approached directly are D and D'. Carbon atom D in the molecule labeled in Fig. 7.1a is only 2.67 Å from the hydrogen atom F of the molecule almost directly above it, and it is interesting that this carbon D is one that deviates most from planarity, being pushed down 0.012 Å out of the plane of its molecule.

The long axes of the molecules are all parallel at about 9° from the c axis of the crystal. Alternate molecules in a given layer do

---

[1] For the sake of clarity in the illustration, the hydrogen atoms were not shown, so that only the skeletons of the molecules appear, and it is therefore not so evident that they are packed closely together.

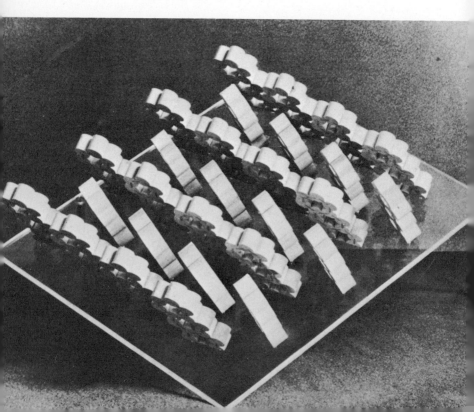

not have their planes parallel, so that viewed along the *a* axis the structure appears as interleaved rows parallel to each other. This arrangement is shown in the model in Fig. 7.1c.

The bond distances within an anthracene molecule are also shown in Fig. 7.1. In accord with the different possible "resonance structures," the bonds have "double-bond characters" from 25 to 75% (3). The bond lengths range from 1.43 to 1.36 Å, compared with the 1.54 and 1.30 Å of pure single and double bonds, respectively.

7.2 COHESIVE ENERGY OF ANTHRACENE CRYSTALS

What are the forces that cause molecules of anthracene to condense and pack together into a crystal? They have been called van der Waals forces because they also cause the departures from ideality in gases that lead to the cohesive term a/V^2 in the van der Waals equation of state, $(P + a/V^2)(V - b) = RT$.

If the molecules had permanent dipole moments, it would be easy to see how they could attract one another, the positive end of one dipole attracting the negative end of another, and vice versa. The field at a distance r from a dipole of moment μ is μ/r^3. But even when molecules are completely nonpolar, like argon or anthracene, van der Waals attractive forces are still present. By lowering temperature and increasing pressure we can liquefy and solidify any gas.

An understanding of these attractive forces between nonpolar molecules was first provided by London in 1930 through a clever application of quantum mechanics. He pointed out that even if a molecule has no permanent dipole moment, nevertheless, at any instant the centers of charge of its negative electrons and positive nuclei would not be likely to coincide. If we could take an instantaneous snapshot of an argon atom, for example, we would find that the electrons were situated so as to give an unsymmetrical distribution of negative charge about the nucleus. Such a snapshot would reveal an instantaneous dipole moment even in an argon atom. Over any appreciable interval of time, these momentary dipoles would average to zero, so that there is no observable net dipole moment.

The way in which momentary dipoles on neighboring molecules produce attractive forces, now called London forces, is quite
subtle. You cannot simply assume that dipoles on two neighboring
molecules attract each other, since at any instant they are just as
likely to be oriented so as to repel as to attract. London realized,
however, that a momentary dipole on one molecule would in-
stantaneously *induce* a dipole in its neighbor, and this induced
dipole must always be oriented so as to attract the original dipole
that induced it. We can see this result from the fact that the negative end of the induced dipole must be closer to the positive end of
the original dipole, which has attracted electrons in the neighboring molecule. The dipole moment induced by an electric field E is
proportional to the field, or equal to αE, where the proportionality
factor α is called the polarizability. The field E due to a dipole of
moment μ is proportional to μ/r^3, so that the dipole μ' induced in
one molecule by a momentary dipole μ on the other is $\alpha\mu/r^3$ and
interaction of this with the original μ has a potential energy
$V = \mu\alpha^2/r^6$. London calculated the instantaneous dipole μ from
quantum mechanics (4). The final result for the attractive potential energy was

$$V \text{ (London)} = -\frac{3}{4}\frac{\alpha^2 I}{r^6} \tag{7.1}$$

Here I is the *ionization potential*, the energy required to remove an
electron completely from the molecule.

In case the two interacting molecules are different, Eq. (7.1)
becomes

$$V = -\frac{3}{2}\frac{\alpha_1\alpha_2}{r^6}\frac{I_1 I_2}{I_1 + I_2} \tag{7.2}$$

This London energy is by far the major contribution to the
cohesive energy of anthracene crystals. In a large aromatic molecule like anthracene, the π electrons in the rings are easily polarized
and these electrons make the major contribution to the London
energy. The heat of sublimation of anthracene is only 22 kcal
mole^{-1}, a fairly typical value for the cohesive energy of a molecular
crystal held together by London forces. By comparison the co-

hesive energy of a typical covalent crystal like silicon is 85 kcal mole^{-1}, and of a typical ionic crystal like rock salt, 183 kcal mole^{-1}.

7.3 OPTICAL ABSORPTION SPECTRA

If we trace the absorption spectrum of an anthracene crystal in the ultraviolet region, we see many features that resemble those of corresponding bands in the spectrum of anthracene in the vapor or in dilute solution in a nonabsorbing solvent. In certain respects, however, the spectrum of the crystal is strikingly different. The interpretation of these differences has provided some of the most fascinating problems in the study of the organic solid state.

The experimental results are summarized in Fig. 7.2, where crystal spectra are colored curves and the spectrum in solution in isooctane is a black curve. The spectra are plotted as molar extinction coefficients ϵ versus the reciprocal wavelength λ^{-1} of the radiation in wave numbers,[2] cm^{-1}. Let us recall that

$$I = I_0 \exp(-\epsilon c x) \tag{7.3}$$

where I_0 is the intensity of incident light and I is the intensity of light transmitted through a thickness x of material in which the concentration of absorbing molecules is c mole liter^{-1}. This equation is used to obtain values of ϵ for anthracene crystals when the light is appropriately polarized and the crystal suitably aligned.

A frequency ($\nu = c/\lambda$) in an absorption band[3] is proportional to the energy $h\nu$ of the quantum of light absorbed when the molecule makes a transition from its ground state to an excited state. In the case of these ultraviolet absorption spectra, the energies $h\nu$ correspond to excitation of an electron in the molecule to some excited state, which may be represented by ψ^e, an excited-state wave function. It is well to distinguish these electronic spectra from absorption spectra in the infrared region, in which no electronic excitation is involved and the spectra are due to vibrational energies of the molecule or crystal. (Compare, for example, the discussion of vibrational spectra of ionic crystals in Section 1.12.)

The crystal spectra depend markedly on the direction of polarization of the light used, with respect to the directions of the

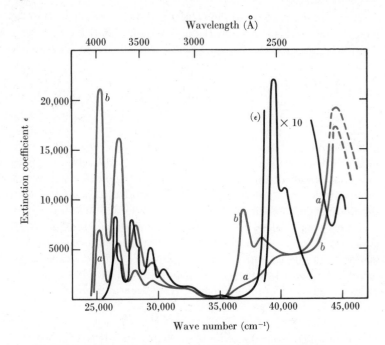

Wavelength (Å)

Fig. 7.2. Absorption spectra of anthracene. The black curve shows absorption from a solution in isooctane. The (red) curves are crystal spectra measured with polarized light. In spectra _a_ the electric vector of the polarized light was in the _ac_ plane. In spectra _b_ the electric vector was parallel to the _b_ axis. Bree and Lyons (5).

crystal axes. Therefore, two crystal spectra are shown, _a_ and _b_, in which the incident light is polarized parallel to the _a_ and _b_ axes of the unit cell, respectively. In the _a_ spectra, the plane of polarization of the light (which is the plane in which the electric field vector

---

[2] One often refers to the "frequency" $\bar{\nu}$ in wave numbers, although actually frequency $\nu = c\bar{\nu} = c/\lambda$.

[3] The spectra appear as bands rather than lines because there is a range of vibrational energies corresponding to each level of electronic energy. We are concerned here only with the interpretation of the electronic energy levels.

of the electromagnetic wave vibrates) lies parallel to the *ac* plane plane of the crystal structure (Fig. 7.1). In the *b* spectra the vibrating electric field is polarized in a plane normal to the *ac* plane and containing the *b* axis of the crystal structure.

The intense bands between 3500 and 4000 Å are observed in solution as well as in the crystal. Both *a* and *b* spectra are shifted definitely toward longer wavelength in the crystal (red shift), but the *b* spectra are more intense than the *a* spectra.

The most intense absorption in solution is the band system at about 2500 Å. Analysis shows that in the crystal this system has been split into two components. In the one centered at about 2700 Å (red shift) the *b* spectra are much more intense than the *a*. The component centered at about 1900 Å (blue shift) was not detected in the first measurements, because it lies in the *vacuum ultraviolet;* this component thus requires the use of a spectrometer operating in high vacuum for its detection, since air absorbs strongly in this region. Lyons and Morris (6) in 1959 extended the measurements into this region and discovered the second component as shown. In this component, the more intense spectrum is that polarized in the *a* direction.

Before we consider any theoretical interpretation of these remarkable spectral effects in anthracene crystals, we should recall the classical model for the absorption of electromagnetic radiation. According to this, the vibrating electric field of the radiation interacts with the electronic charge distribution of the molecule to produce an oscillating dipole (separated positive and negative charge), which can absorb energy from the radiation field when its natural vibration frequency resonates with that of the incident radiation. In the quantum mechanical theory, light absorption is not explained entirely by such an oscillating dipole but is formulated in terms of two requirements:

(1) There must be a ground state and an excited state of the molecule, represented by wave functions ψ_1 and ψ_2, whose respective energies satisfy the condition,

$$h\nu = E_2 - E_1$$

where ν is the frequency of the radiation absorbed.

(2) If condition (1) is satisfied, the intensity of the absorption

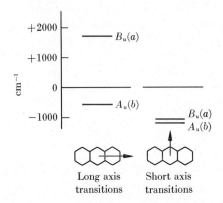

Fig. 7.3. Energy levels for anthracene in the crystal calculated for transitions of 1 Å dipole length polarized along the *a* and *b* crystal axes. Craig and Walmsley (8).

band will be determined by the value of the so-called *transition moment* M_{12}, which can be written as a dipole moment μ averaged between the ground and excited states,

$$M_{12} = \int \psi_1 \mu \psi_2 \, dx \, dy \, dz \qquad (7.4)$$

Note that the molecule need not have a permanent dipole moment in the ground state for electronic excitation to occur by absorption of a light quantum. It is sufficient that M_{12} have a finite value. This second condition replaces the classical model of the oscillating dipole. The first condition drastically restricts the allowed spectral frequencies.

It is worth remarking that these transition dipoles that occur during electronic excitations are the same as the momentary dipoles described in connection with London forces.

In a long planar molecule like anthracene the transition dipoles must have definite directions relative to the axes of the molecule. We thus classify transitions in the isolated molecule as *long-axis transitions* and *short-axis transitions*, as shown in Fig. 7.3. These classifications would apply just as well to gas spectra as to crystal spectra. Only in the crystal, however, are the molecules held in regular places so that we can fix experimentally a definite angle between the molecular axes (as determined by the crystal axes) and the plane of polarization of the radiation absorbed.

7.4 EXCITONS—DAVYDOV THEORY

The concept of an *exciton*, a localized electronic excitation in a crystal, was first discovered about 30 years ago, independently by Peierls and Frenkel. In 1948 the Russian physicist, Davydov, gave a good quantitative theory (7), which has been the basis of much important work on crystal spectra, photoconductivity, and energy-transfer through solids.

We can introduce the basic ideas of the Davydov theory by looking at a simple model based on two identical molecules only, A and B. If these molecules are far apart, there is no interaction between them, and their absorption spectrum is that characteristic of a gas or dilute solution. We could write their wave function as $\psi_G = \psi_A \psi_B$. If the molecules approach closer together, as in a crystal, a certain overlap in their electronic charge distributions begins to occur. When the molecules are fairly close to each other, say 5 or 10 Å, suppose that one of the B absorbs a quantum $h\nu$ of radiation and becomes excited to a higher electronic energy. We can write the resultant wave function as

$$\psi_E = \psi_A \psi_B{}^e$$

where ψ_A is the ground-state wave function of molecule A and $\psi_B{}^e$ is the excited-state wave function of molecule B. Since the molecules A and B are chemically identical, there is no reason why the excitation should be localized on B rather than on A, as long as the molecules are close enough together to allow some overlap and electrical interaction. We must admit, therefore, that an equally good wave function would be

$$\psi'_E = \psi_A{}^e \psi_B$$

When we have two "identical" interacting states such as ψ_E and ψ'_E we know that the correct wave function for the system is a linear combination of the two degenerate functions, which can be written as

$$\psi_I = 2^{-1/2}(\psi_E + \psi'_E)$$

or

$$\psi_{II} = 2^{-1/2}(\psi_E - \psi'_E) \qquad (7.5)$$

Note that in both these wave functions the excitation is shared between the two molecules and not localized. The $2^{-1/2}$ is a *normalization factor* to allow both ψ_I and ψ_E to represent wave functions that give the correct total charge for the electrons. The energy level of the isolated molecule splits into two energy levels, one somewhat higher and one somewhat lower than the original:

$$E_I = E - \Delta E$$
$$E_{II} = E + \Delta E \qquad (7.6)$$

In the study of the chemical bond, ΔE is often called a *resonance energy*.

The interaction between molecules A and B that causes the resonance energy ΔE is a dipole-dipole interaction, predominantly between states terminating allowed transitions. As explained in the previous section, even if the molecule has no permanent dipole moment, there will be a *transition moment*, as given by Eq. (7.4), for any allowed electronic transition caused by absorption of light. It is the dipole-dipole interaction between these transition moments that causes the *Davydov splitting* ΔE. The interaction will depend on the angles between the transition moments on the two molecules

$$\Delta E = \frac{-M^2}{r^3}\left(2\cos\theta_A^z\cos\theta_B^z - \cos\theta_A^x\cos\theta_B^x \right.$$
$$\left. - \cos\theta_A^y\cos\theta_B^y\right) \quad (7.7)$$

Here θ_A^z, for example, is the angle made by the transition moment on molecule A with the z axis, and so on. In an actual crystal, these angles depend on the mutual orientation of the molecules in the crystal structure and on the directions of the transtition moments in these molecules. The Davydov interaction varies as r^{-3} (rather than r^{-6}) since the dipoles are fixed in magnitude and orientation.

The dependence on distance is therefore not the same as that between tumbling permanent dipoles in a gas, or between the dipoles and induced dipoles that are responsible for London forces. As a consequence, the Davydov interaction in an exciton can be appreciable even at distances at which London forces are small.

Let us consider a simple case in which the transition dipoles in a pair of molecules are both parallel to the x axis. Then Eq. (7.7) becomes

$$\Delta E = \frac{M^2}{r^3_{AB}} \tag{7.8}$$

The resultant splitting of the energy levels is as follows:

$$\psi_{II} = 2^{-1/2}(\psi_A \psi_B^e - \psi_A^e \psi_B)$$

$\psi_E = \psi_A \psi_B^e \qquad \psi_E' = \psi_A^e \psi_B \qquad \Delta E$

ΔE

$$\psi_I = 2^{-1/2}(\psi_A \psi_B^e + \psi_A^e \psi_B)$$

$$\psi_G = \psi_A \psi_B$$

Note particularly from Eq. (7.8) that the larger the transition moment M, that is, the more intense the absorption band, the larger will be the Davydov splitting ΔE.

When more detailed calculations were made for anthracene on this model, the energy levels shown in Fig. 7.3 were obtained. In these calculations interactions between all the molecules in the crystal were considered, not just those between a pair. For the more intense long-axis transition, two energy levels were found, one above the unperturbed level (polarized parallel to b axis of crystal) and one below (polarized parallel to a axis of crystal). In the case of the considerably weaker short-axis transition, the two levels (a and b polarized) were very close together and were both displaced to lower energies.

We can now understand the anthracene crystal spectrum shown in Fig. 7.2. The intense bands at 2700 Å and 1900 Å are the long-axis spectra, showing a blue shift for the a polarized transition and a red shift for the b polarized transition. The band system centered around 3750 Å is related to the less intense short-axis excitation of the molecule, and both components *a* and *b* display a red shift as predicted. Note that in this case *b* is more intense than *a* since the molecules are so oriented in the crystal that light polarized normal to the *ac* plane has an electric vector more nearly parallel to the short axis of the molecule.

7.5 LUMINESCENCE

The emission of light when an excited system returns to the ground state is called *luminescence*. A molecule or crystal can become excited in various ways: light absorption, electron bombardment, application of a strong electric field, thermal excitation

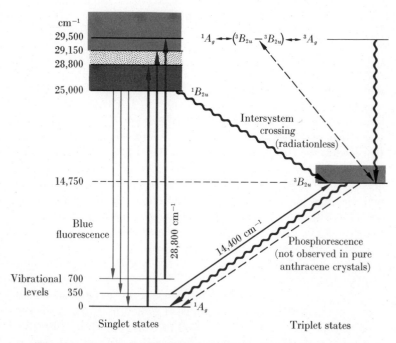

Fig. 7.4. Energy levels of anthracene crystals, showing some of the transitions that have been studied. Singh *et al.* (9).

due to adiabatic compression in a shock wave, ultrasonic absorption. There is also *chemiluminescence*, in which the excited state is the product of a chemical reaction. Thus luminescence covers many fascinating phenomena of great theoretical and practical importance.

From a theoretical viewpoint, excitation by light absorption is especially useful, since in this case the exact nature of the excited state can often be specified. Two sets of states are distinguished, singlets and triplets, as shown in Fig. 7.4. The ground state of an organic molecule or crystal is usually a *singlet state*, that is, there are no unpaired spins. The excited state reached is also usually a singlet, since there is only a small probability that the process of light absorption will uncouple the electron spins.[4] If the system returns directly from the lowest singlet excited state to the ground state by emission of a light quantum $h\nu$, the luminescent emission is called *fluorescence*. In the second case, as shown in Fig. 7.4 the excited system undergoes a radiationless transition to a lower-lying triplet state. In a crystal, such a transition can be rapid, as the excess energy can be taken up into the vibrations of the crystal structure. If this excited triplet now emits a quantum $h\nu$ and returns to the ground state, the luminescent emission is called *phosphorescence*.

In earlier days a distinction between fluorescence and phosphorescence was based on the lifetimes of the excited states, which determined the rate of decay of the light emission following excitation of the system. If the emission of light continued for a longish time, it was called *phosphorescence;* if it was soon over, it was called *luminescence*. These definitions are no longer in use. It is true, however, that the lifetimes for fluorescence, typically 10^{-9} to 10^{-6} sec, are usually much shorter than those for phosphorescence, normally in the range 10^{-3} to 1 sec. There are exceptions to this rule, however, and the accepted nomenclature now follows strictly the spectroscopic identification of the states.

Luminescent decay times can be measured with a *phosphoro-*

---

[4] In the diagram of Fig. 7.4, the singlet-triplet absorption is shown, because the light source used to obtain these data was a high-intensity laser emitting up to 10^{27} photons cm^{-2} sec^{-1} and hence appreciable singlet-to-triplet absorption took place despite its low probability per quantum absorbed.

scope, described by Becquerel in 1867. Two disks with sectorial slits are mounted on the same shaft. The sample is placed between the disks. The slits are offset so that when the sample is illuminated through a slit in one disk, the light is blocked by the second disk. The shaft is now rapidly rotated, and when the time of decay of luminescence or phosphorescence is matched with the rotational time between the offset slits, the light emission from the sample can pass through the slits and be recorded. A mechanical phosphoroscope driven at 10^4 rpm would be suitable for lifetimes as low as $\tau = 10^{-6}$ sec, but this is about the limit of such an instrument.

Figure 7.5 shows the equipment used to obtain the data on energy levels shown in Fig. 7.4 as well as on the transition rates between these levels by various processes. The radiation source for this equipment was the 4943 Å (14,400 cm^{-1}) radiation from a giant-pulse ruby laser, which emitted a pulse of about 30×10^{-9} sec duration at a power of 10^6 to 10^7 watts. The crystal was placed between the two metal sector disks which were rotated on a common axis at 4000 rpm.[5] This arrangement allowed the laser beam itself to be stopped by a blackened area of disk B after it had passed through disk A and the crystal. The offset holes in disk B allowed successive measurements at equal time intervals to be made of the long-lived fluorescence from the crystal. The fast fluorescence was measured by removing the disks and placing a photomultiplier tube at right angles to the laser beam.

The short-lived fluorescence decayed exponentially with a half-life $\tau = 2.1 \times 10^{-8}$ sec. This corresponds to decay of the singlet exciton formed by the transition from the ^1A_g ground state to the $^1B_{2u}$ excited state. Note that this transition required an absorption of two quanta of the laser radiation. Such two-quanta absorption processes were never observable with ordinary light sources, but can occur with laser beams owing to the extremely high flux of photons through the sample. The lifetime of this singlet exciton would be just the same, however, if it was produced by the more conventional absorption of a single quantum of ultraviolet light.

---

[5] The use of rotating disks in this equipment recalls the phosphoroscope but their function here is somewhat different from that in Becquerel's device.

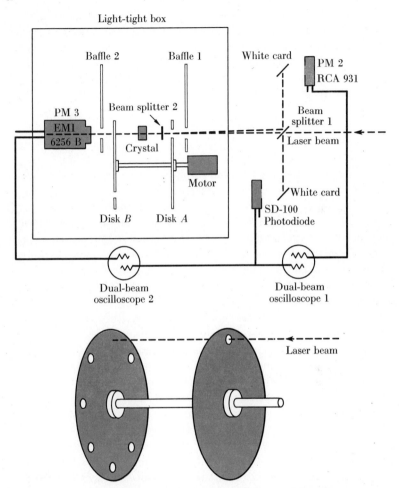

Fig. 7.5.   An experimental arrangement for studying fluorescent lifetimes in solid anthracene.   Singh *et al.* (9).

The decay of the long-lived blue fluorescence followed a rather complex kinetics with a limiting half-life of 2 to 20×10^{-3} sec, depending on the purity of the anthracene.   The processes involved here are, first, a radiationless transfer of the singlet-singlet excitation energy to the lowest triplet state, $^3B_{2u}$, followed by a recombination of two triplet excitons to yield a singlet, followed in turn by emission of the blue fluorescent light. With anthracene crystals, no phosphorescent emission was detected from the triplet $^3B_{2u}$ state, but it has frequently been observed from anthracene dispersed in solid benzene.

7.6   EXCITATION-ENERGY TRANSFER

If a crystal of very pure anthracene is illuminated with ultraviolet light at 3400 Å, it emits a pale blue fluorescence, as a consequence of the singlet-singlet transition described in the previous section. A crystal of very pure tetracene, similarly irradiated, emits a bright green fluorescence. If we dissolve in the anthracene crystal as little as one part in 10^4 of tetracene, an astonishing phenomenon occurs. The blue anthracene fluorescence is suppressed completely and the green fluorescence of tetracene appears. Although almost all the light has been absorbed by anthracene molecules, fluorescent emission occurs almost entirely from the few tetracene molecules dispersed in the anthracene crystal. If we raise the temperature, no change occurs until the crystal melts, when exactly at the melting point, the green tetracene fluorescence is extinguished and the pale blue anthracene fluorescence reappears.

It is evident that by some mechanism the energy of excitation of anthracene can dart swiftly through the crystal (but not through the liquid) until it is captured by the rare molecule of tetracene, there to be emitted as a quantum of fluorescent radiation.

One possible mechanism for this transfer of excitation energy may be eliminated at once. It cannot be caused simply by reemission of radiation by the anthracene and its absorption by the tetracene. With such a mechanism, the very small concentration of tetracene molecules in the anthracene crystal would, on geometrical grounds alone, allow most of the reemitted radiation to be lost.

An ingenious experiment by Simpson (10) gave a quantitative measure of the distance over which the excitation energy could be transferred. Layers of pure anthracene of varying thickness were evaporated on top of crystals of anthracene doped with tetracene. The pure anthracene surface was then irradiated with light in the anthracene absorption band. The thickness of pure anthracene was determined which was just sufficient to prevent the excitation from reaching the doped crystal and giving the green fluorescence. In this way, the diffusion length of the excitation was found to be about 400 Å.

The transfer of excitation energy over such a long distance suggests clearly that the exciton can be considered to have a high mobility. The exciton can jump rapidly from molecule to molecule in the crystal, since there will always be a state localized on a neighboring molecule that will have just as acceptable a wave function as the original state. From the uncertainty principle, $\Delta E \cdot \Delta \tau \sim h$, the time the exciton resides on any one molecule is of the order of $\Delta \tau = h / \Delta E$ where ΔE is here the width of the band of allowed energy levels for the exciton. We have seen from the absorption spectrum that this ΔE, the Davydov splitting, is about $\bar{\nu} = 100$ cm^{-1} for the near ultraviolet absorption band. This $\bar{\nu}$ would correspond to $\Delta \tau = h/(hc\bar{\nu}) = 3.3 \times 10^{-13}$ sec. Even with a lifetime of the excited state as low as 10^{-9} sec, the exciton could make 3.3×10^4 jumps, or, since the mean diffusional distance depends on the square root of the number of jumps, it could travel on the average $(3.3 \times 10^4)^{1/2} = 180$ interatomic distances, or several hundred angstroms. We can conclude that such a model is quite attractive for the observed fluorescent behavior of the doped anthracene crystal. The exciton hops merrily about the crystal until it is captured by a tetracene molecule. In the absence of an impurity like tetracene, it is likely that capture and reemission occurs at some defect site in the structure, such as a dislocation.

We should mention that there is another mechanism of energy transfer which may be important in certain cases, the Förster mechanism of *direct resonance transfer*. This can occur between either like or unlike molecules, so long as the fluorescence spectrum of the donor molecule D overlaps the absorption spectrum of the acceptor A. Provided there is an energetic coupling between the molecules, D can then simply hand its energy over to A, without the intervention of any emission or absorption. The coupling responsible for this transfer is exactly the same as that effective in

London forces, and hence varies as R^{-6}. We should therefore not expect this Förster mechanism to be effective over distances longer than about 50 Å. This point was checked for anthracene and tetracene in an experiment in which they were both dissolved in low concentrations in a host crystal of naphthalene, and the usual irradiation carried out in the anthracene absorption band. Under these conditions, exciton migration is impossible, since the anthracene has no neighbors of its own species. It was found experimentally that the limiting range of energy transfer was then about 44 Å, in good agreement with the Förster model.

Such processes of long-range energy transfer, so well exemplified by the anthracene-tetracene system, may be of importance in biological processes such as photosynthesis and visual perception.

7.7   PHOTOCONDUCTIVITY

The electrical conductivity σ of anthracene in the dark is very low, and the more you purify the substance, the lower its σ becomes. At room temperature for purest anthracene σ may be as low as 10^{-18} ohm^{-1} cm^{-1}. Various measurements indicate that the temperature dependence is $\sigma = \sigma_0 \exp(-\epsilon/2kT)$ as would be expected for a semiconductor. Because of the marked effects of impurities—including probably oxygen from the air, ϵ is not known very accurately, but is about 3.4 eV. From our experience with inorganic semiconductors (Section 3.2) we should expect this ϵ to be close to the energy gap between a valence band and a conduction band, but no such simple relation can be established for anthracene. It is concluded that the electrons and holes responsible for conductivity are not the result of excitation across a band gap but arise from impurities, from the surface of the crystal, or by injection from the contact electrodes used in the experimental setup.

When anthracene is illuminated with light in one of its absorption bands, its conductivity is greatly increased. We are not sure exactly how irradiation increases the number of charge carriers and hence the conductivity but the evidence favors a sequence of events something like the following. On absorption of a light quantum,

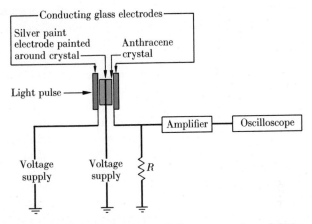

Fig. 7.6. Experiment of Kepler (11) to measure mobilities of electrons and holes in anthracene.

an exciton may be produced in the crystal and, as we have seen, it will be quite mobile. This exciton can be visualized as an excited electron bound to a positive hole in the valence band. It will hop about through the crystal until it strikes either the surface or some kind of trapping center T. It may then dissociate in either of two ways:

$$e^- - p + T \rightarrow p - T + e^-$$
$$e^- - p + T' \rightarrow e^- - T' + p$$

In this way free charge carriers are released, which in an electric field yield the observed photocurrents. In anthracene, the majority carriers are the positive holes. Let us recall, from Eq. (3.5) that the conductivity

$$\sigma = e(N_e \mu_e + N_h \mu_h)$$

The next interesting problem, therefore, is to measure the mobilities of the electrons and holes. Figure 7.6 shows the experiment devised by Kepler (11) in 1960 to make this measurement. The anthracene crystal was mounted between conducting transparent electrodes. These were plates of glass or silica coated with a thin layer of stannic oxide. The stannic oxide makes electrical contact with the organic crystal but does not greatly decrease the transparency of the electrode. Thus it is possible to illuminate the specimen directly through the electrodes. Kepler also painted a ring of silver around the crystal, as an auxiliary electrode which permitted him to study the charge on the current carriers while they were passing through the crystal. When the illuminated electrode was negative, only negative carriers were injected into the anthracene and traversed the crystal. When the illuminated electrode was positive, only positive carriers passed through the crystal. The experiment now consisted in illuminating the crystal through one electrode with a short flash and measuring the time required for the carriers to cross the crystal and produce a current pulse on the oscilloscope. Since mobility is velocity per unit field ($\mu = v/F$), the time taken for carriers to traverse a thickness d of crystal is

$$t = \frac{d}{v} = \frac{d}{\mu F}$$

Kepler found that at 25°C the mobilities perpendicular to the *ab* plane were 0.4 cm^2 V^{-1} sec^{-1} for holes and 0.3 cm^2 V^{-1} sec^{-1} for electrons. Parallel to the *ab* plane, the mobilities were $\mu_h = 1.3$ and $\mu_e = 2.0$.

One successful application of photoconductivity has been the Xerox reproduction process. This uses a screen of selenium which is a good photoconductor, but the same effect has been seen with anthracene. The surface of the screen is charged electrically by spraying negative charges over it from a source of ionization. It is then exposed to light from a black-on-white page that is to be copied. Where the light strikes the photoconductive screen, it renders it conducting and the electrostatic charges are removed from these areas. The screen is now dusted with a carbonaceous dry ink whose particles are probably positively charged. The ink particles adhere only to the undischarged negative regions of the plate, thereby forming a dry-inked master from which successive copies can be taken by contact with white paper.

It seems likely that the next few years will bring further applications of photoconductivity in printing and reproduction processes. Considering the vast number of organic compounds, metal-organics, and polymers, we may suppose that the organic solid state will provide many new discoveries and inventions in this field and in solid state electronics.

REFERENCES

(1) A. Szent-Györgyi, *Introduction to a Submolecular Biology* (New York: Academic Press, 1960), Chapter V.

(2) D. W. J. Cruickshank, *Acta Cryst.* 9, 915 (1956).

(3) L. Pauling, *The Nature of the Chemical Bond* (Ithaca, N.Y.: Cornell University Press, 1960), pp. 198, 237.

(4) A concise derivation is given by J. C. Slater, *Quantum Theory of Matter* (New York: McGraw-Hill, 1951), p. 396.

(5) A. V. Bree and L. E. Lyons, *J. Chem. Soc.* 1960, 5206.

(6) L. E. Lyons and G. C. Morris, *J. Chem. Soc.* 1959, 1551.

(7) M. Kasha has described the theory and its applications in three excellent articles for the nonspecialist reader: (1) "The Molecular Exciton Model" (with E. G. McRae), in *Physical Processes in Radiation Biology* (New York: Academic Press, 1964); (2) "Lamellar Excitons" (with R. Hochstrasser), *Photochem. Photobiol.* 3, 317 (1964); (3) "Energy Transfer Mechansims," *Radiation Res.* 20, 55 (1963).

(8) D. P. Craig and S. H. Walmsley, *Physics and Chemistry of the Organic Solid State* (New York: Interscience, 1963), Chapter X.

(9) S. Singh, W. J. Jones, W. Siebrand, B. P. Stoicheff, and W. G. Schneider, *J. Chem. Phys.* 42, 330 (1965).

(10) O. Simpson, *Proc. Roy. Soc. (London)* A238, 402 (1956).

(11) R. G. Kepler, *Phys. Rev.* 119, 1226 (1960).

Problems

1. Draw a primitive square lattice and a centered square lattice. Determine the densities of points in the rows with Miller indices (10), (11), (21), (31), and (32). Compare these densities with the distances between the rows.

2. Show graphically that fivefold axes are inconsistent with translational symmetry.

3. A crystal plane intercepts the three crystallographic axes at the following multiples of the unit distances: 3/2, 2, 1. What are the Miller indices of the plane?

4. With x rays of wavelength 1.540 Å it was found that the first "reflection" from a KCl crystal occurred at $\theta = 14°12'$. Calculate the length of the unit cell and the density of the crystal.

5. By means of drawings show the [110], [1$\bar{1}$1], and [212] directions in a cubic unit cell.

6. Show, by drawing, that the face-centered cubic lattice can also be represented as a rhombohedral lattice with $\alpha = 60°$.

7. The Madelung energy of NaF (NaCl structure) is 248.1 kcal mole^{-1}. Calculate the nearest cation-anion distance and the length of the unit cell.

8. Suppose that a crystal of NaCl has a concentration of 10^{-3} atom fraction of (a) Schottky and (b) Frenkel defects. Calculate the densities of crystals at 25°C for these two cases.

9. A problem of interest to geologists is whether diffusion of ions in minerals can be responsible for changes in structures over appreciable distances. We can estimate a mean distance $\bar{x}$ of diffusion from $\bar{x} = (2Dt)^{1/2}$. Using the value given on p. 35 for the D of Na^+ in NaCl estimate the mean diffusion distance of Na^+ in a rock salt crystal over a period of 10^6 years at 30°C.

CHAPTER 2

1. Calculate the distance between the centers of gold atoms at 25°C in the 100, 110, and 111 planes of the crystal structure ($a_0 = 4.070$ Å).

2. Assuming the 111 planes of gold structure are closest packed, estimate the diameter of a gold atom considered as a rigid sphere. Hence calculate the diameter of the largest interstitial void space in the gold structure.

3. The Fermi level of gold is 5.51 eV. Plot the Fermi-Dirac distribution function of Eq. (2.7) (P versus E) for $T = 100°$ and $1000°K$.

4. What is the approximate concentration of vacancies in a crystal of gold at its melting point if the energy of formation of a vacancy equals one half the latent heat of sublimation?

5. Equation (2.11) gives the number of states per unit volume $N(E)$ as a function of E. At $0°K$, where all the states are occupied up to the value of Fermi energy E_F, the number of electrons per unit volume $N = \int_0^{E_F} N(E) \, dE$. Show therefore that $E_F(0°K) = (h^2/8\pi^2 m) \, (3\pi^2 N)^{2/3}$.

6. The electrical conductivity of gold at 25°C is 4.7×10^5 ohm^{-1} cm^{-1} and the Hall constant is -7.2×10^{-11} volt cm amp^{-1} oersted^{-1}. Calculate the mobility of the conduction electrons in gold. How does this figure compare with the mobility of a Na^+ ion in a dilute solution of NaCl in water? (Hall effect is discussed in Chapter 3.)

7. Show that the average value of the energy of an electron in a Fermi gas is $\bar{E} = \frac{3}{5} E_F$. (The formula for computing an average value of a property r over a distribution function $p(r)$ is

$$\bar{r} = \int_0^{r_{max}} r p(r) \, dr \Big/ \int_0^{r_{max}} p(r) \, dr$$

8. Assuming one conduction electron per atom in a metal with the dimensions of the copper crystal structure, find the maximum kinetic energy of the electrons in electron volts, if they act like free electrons in a box.

9. Consider the quantum numbers $n^2 = n_x^2 + n_y^2 + n_z^2$. They are defined for positive and negative $\mathbf{k}_n$, and surfaces of equal energy are spheres. Indicate how the degeneracy (number of levels with the same energy) depends on n.

10. Show that the time-dependent solution of the wave equation

$$\psi(x, t) = e^{i[(E/h)t - kx]}$$

represents a wave traveling in the positive x direction with phase velocity E/hk. What is the group velocity? According to the de Broglie relation, what momentum is associated with the wave?

CHAPTER 3

1. The unit cell side in the silicon structure is $a_0 = 5.430$ Å at 25°C. Calculate the nearest and next nearest distances between centers of silicon atoms.

2. From Fig. 3.3 and Eq. (3.11) calculate the thermal band gaps in Si and Ge.

3. Consider silicon crystals (band gap 1.06 eV) in which are dissolved donor phosphorus atoms at total concentrations of 10^{17}, 10^{16}, 10^{15} cm^{-3}. The ionization energy of the donor is 0.012 eV, and the effective density of states in the conduction band is $N_c = 10^{15} \times T^{3/2}$. Use Eq. (3.6) to calculate the equilibrium concentration of electrons in the conduction band at various temperatures between 78°K (liquid nitrogen) and 600°K.

4. Using results from Problem 3, plot the log of conductivity

($\log \sigma$) versus T^{-1} for the doped crystals assuming that the mobility of the electrons is $\mu = 5 \times 10^6 T^{-3/2}$ cm^2 volt^{-1} sec^{-1}.

5. If the silicon crystal is so pure that only intrinsic conductivity need be considered, calculate $\log \sigma$ versus T^{-1} between 78° and 600°K assuming $\mu_- = \mu_+$.

6. Calculate the Hall coefficient of the crystal in Problem 5 at 300°K.

7. What is the drift velocity of the conduction electrons in silicon at 300°K in an electric field of 100 volt cm^{-1}?

CHAPTER 4

1. The Clapeyron-Clausius equation for variation of transition temperature T with pressure is $dT/dP = T \Delta V/\Delta H$. Apply this to the $\alpha \rightleftharpoons \gamma$ transition of iron to calculate ΔH, the enthalpy change of the transition, from the data given in last paragraph of Section 4.1.

2. Suppose a melt containing 8 atom % carbon in pure iron is suddenly quenched to 800°C. Describe quantitatively the compositions of the equilibrium solid phases that will be formed (use Fig. 4.3).

3. The unit cell of α-Fe has a length $a_0 = 2.861$ Å at 25°C. The coefficient of linear expansion of iron from 0° to 900°C can be estimated as 1.2×10^{-5}. Calculate the value of a_0 for α-Fe at 906°C, the transition temperature to γ-Fe. From the value $\Delta V = 0.001$ cm^3 g^{-1} for volume change on transition to γ-Fe, calculate the a_0 of the unit cell of γ-Fe at the transition T. Calculate the nearest distance between centers of Fe atoms for both α-Fe and γ-Fe at the transition temperature.

4. The Curie-Weiss law for the temperature dependence of the paramagnetic susceptibility χ is $C/\chi = T - T_c$, where T_c is the Curie temperature and $C = Nn^2\mu_B^2/3k$ (N is atoms cm^{-3}, n is effective number of Bohr magnetons μ_B per atom, k is the Boltzmann constant). The following values of χ were measured for Fe above its Curie temperature.

T°K:	1097	1119	1145	1167	1177
χ:	0.00683	0.00316	0.00269	0.00209	0.00194

Calculate T_c and n for paramagnetic α-Fe.

5. Consider a simple cubic crystal structure in which there are two parallel edge dislocations moving in two parallel slip planes separated by one vertical translation. If one dislocation lying above its slip plane moves toward the other lying below its slip plane, what happens when they meet? (See Fig. 4.8a.)

CHAPTER 5

1. Calculate the nearest Ni-Ni distances in NiO and Ni at 25°C given that the lengths of "cubic" unit cells are 3.517 and 4.180 Å, respectively.

2. Consider again the theory of the Madelung energy in Chapter 1. Calculate the change in electrostatic (Madelung) energy in kilocalories per mole produced by replacing two Ni^{3+} ions in NiO by a Li^+ and a Ni^{3+} ion, well separated from each other.

3. The conductivity of a specimen of $Li_xNi_{1-x}O$ with $x = 10^{-3}$ was 10^{-2} ohm^{-1} cm^{-1} at 500°K. Estimate the mobility of positive holes in this material assuming all positive holes introduced into the NiO by doping with Li are free to move.

4. In nearly stoichiometric NiO the mobility of holes at 1000°K was found to be 60 cm^2 volt^{-1} sec^{-1}. Estimate the conductivity of NiO in equilibrium with oxygen at 1 atm pressure and 1000°K if the standard Gibbs function change for reaction $\frac{1}{2}O_2 + Ni^{2+} \rightleftharpoons O^{2-} + Ni^{3+} + V_c$ is $\Delta G^0 = 40$ kcal mole^{-1}.

5. The parabolic rate constant K for oxidation of nickel at 1000°C and 1 atm O_2 is 5.0×10^{-12} cm^2 sec^{-1}. At this temperature and pressure what fraction of the oxygen molecules striking the surface of oxide-covered nickel react to form nickel oxide when the thickness of the NiO film is (a) 100 Å (b) 10^{-2} cm.

6. A sample of nickel foil with a surface area of 1400 cm^2 was exposed to oxygen at 10 cm and 500°C. The oxygen uptake in 10 hr by reaction $Ni + \frac{1}{2}O_2 \rightarrow NiO$ was 6.0 cm^3 at STP. Calculate the parabolic rate constant K of Eq. (5.16) in units of cm^2 sec^{-1}.

CHAPTER 6

1. If the structure of corundum is based on a hexagonal closest packing of oxide ions what is radius of largest sphere that can be fitted into the octahedral sites?

2. The coordination of Al^{3+} in Fig. 6.1c does not appear to be octahedral. Redraw the figure so as to show the distorted octahedral configuration of the site.

3. The $^4P_{1/2}$ state of the isolated Cr^{3+} ion lies 14072 cm^{-1} above the $^4F_{3/2}$ ground state. What is this energy difference in electron volts? What would be the ratio of populations of these states at 2000°K?

4. In discussing the isolated Cr^{3+} ion in the text we neglected the splitting of the states due to spin-orbit interaction (LS coupling), which leads to a new quantum number J with allowed values $L + S$, $L + S - 1$, . . . , $L - S$. Thus the ^4F ground state of Cr^{3+} is split into four states with $J = 3/2, 5/2, 7/2, 9/2$. The energy levels of which are 0, 244, 561, and 956 cm^{-1}. Calculate the relative populations of these levels at 300°K. Compare these spin-orbit interaction energies in isolated Cr^{3+} with the crystal field splitting of ^4F shown in Fig. 6.3.

5. The horizontal component of the earth's magnetic field is about 0.20 gauss. What would be the precession frequency of the magnetic moment of a Cr^{3+} ion in ruby in such a field? Could resonance methods based on paramagnetic ions be used to measure the earth's magnetic field?

6. Compare numerically the spin angular momentum of a free electron with the orbital angular momentum of an electron in a hydrogen atom in the $2p$ state. Compare numerically both these angular momenta with that of the earth.

CHAPTER 7

1. Calculate the density of anthracene at 25°C from the unit cell dimensions given in the text.

2. To get some idea of the order of magnitude of London energies between hydrogen atoms in anthracene ($C_{16}H_{10}$) structure, consider ten H atoms each 3.0 Å from another H atom, and use Eq. (7.1) to estimate the London energy of this configuration. For the H atom, the polarizability is $\alpha = 4.5\ a_0^3$ where a_0 is the radius of Bohr orbit, and $I = 13.53$ eV. What does this calculation suggest about the origin of the cohesive energy of anthracene (about 22 kcal mole^{-1})?

3. The giant-pulse ruby laser mentioned in the text gave a 3×10^{-8} sec pulse of 10^7 watts at 4943 Å wavelength. How many quanta of radiation are in such a pulse?

4. Suppose all the quanta in a pulse like that in Problem 3 could be trapped in a long-lived fluorescent state with half-life of 10^{-3} sec. About how long after the pulse would the fluorescent light be detectable by a dark-adapted human eye sensitive to 5 quanta per millisecond?

5. If the conductivity of pure anthracene at 25°C is 10^{-18} ohm^{-1} cm^{-1}, and the mobilities of holes and electrons are both about 1.0 cm^2 V^{-1} sec^{-1}, estimate the number of current carriers per cm^3, assuming pure anthracene is an intrinsic semiconductor.

6. If the thermal band gap in anthracene is 3.4 eV and excitation of an electron from valence band to conduction band can be considered to occur as a molecular process (i.e., density of donor and acceptor states equals density of anthracene molecules) estimate the concentration of carriers and compare with the value found in Problem 5.

Index